WALTER REED AND YELLOW FEVER

From a photograph taken in 1901.   Ætat 50

WALTER REED
AND YELLOW FEVER

By

HOWARD A. KELLY

PROFESSOR OF GYNECOLOGICAL SURGERY
JOHNS HOPKINS UNIVERSITY

New and Revised Edition

BALTIMORE
THE MEDICAL STANDARD BOOK COMPANY,
PUBLISHERS,

Hal

To
James Carroll
and
to the memory of
Jesse William Lazear
this work of love is affectionately
inscribed

PREFACE TO SECOND EDITION

A SECOND edition within six months! I am indeed glad that Walter Reed and his great work have found such a welcome at the hands of his countrymen. It also gives me great pleasure to know that since this little book has told the simple story of his life, the Memorial Fund has grown almost to completion. The second edition will be found to differ from the first in the correction of certain errata which have been pointed out to me, and, more particularly, in the addition of some letters relating especially to the value of Dr. Carroll's work at Camp Lazear and at Las Animas Hospital. Dr. Carroll, Dr. Reed's faithful associate in all his labors, is still with us; in what way will the American Republic show her appreciation of his devoted service?

H. A. K.

October 26, 1906

PREFACE

MY pleasant self-imposed task is at an end.

I had hoped at the beginning that I might be able to catch enough of that evanescent aura which we call a personality, to convey in written words some clear notion of the man to whom it was given to make the greatest American medical discovery. Alas, as I look upon my unfinished picture, I realise the impossibility of protraying that *"animula blandula, vagula, hospes comesque corporis"*— with us so short a time and then gone. The momentous external activities in which the man was engaged are easily recited, but the real inner man must, I think perhaps in all such attempts, evade the crude methods of the biographer. Only He who gave it can really appreciate the spirit of a man, as only to Him who gave it does that spirit hold itself responsible for its activities during its earthly stewardship. The inspiration of Reed's life lies to me in the fact that, though a man of war, he ravaged no distant lands, he destroyed no tens of thousands to make his reputation, but by quiet methods, when there was no strife, he saved countless lives and swept away a hideous plague, which from time immemorial had periodically visited our shores, devastated our fair land, and too often snatched from the years of peace and plenty all their blessings.

My personal interest, as I reviewed the history of the various yellow fever epidemics in this country, was enhanced by the fact that my two paternal great-grandmothers were sufferers in the Philadelphia epidemic of 1793, in which one of them died. The terrible cries of the men who drove the dead-carts, " Bring out your dead! bring out your dead!" lingered long in the ears of my great-grandmother, Mrs. Thomas Kelly.

Acknowledgments for hearty coöperation are due to Mrs. Walter Reed, for her constant sympathy and ready aid given at every phase of the work. I am indebted to Dr. Reed's sister, the late Mrs. J. H. Blincoe, as well as to his brother, Mr. Christopher Reed, for information relating to his childhood and youth.

Dr. James Carroll, Dr. Reed's friend and fellow commissioner, has furnished me much valuable information relative to the work of the Yellow Fever Commission; while Major J. R. Kean has given cheerful aid in securing data concerning his army life.

I have to thank my friend, Dr. Mary Augusta

Scott, Professor of English in Smith College, for aid in reading and criticising the manuscript.

Dr. Henry M. Hurd, Superintendent of the Johns Hopkins Hospital, has proved a valuable friend and helper on this, as on similar occasions, in giving advice touching additions and alterations.

Professor William H. Welch wrote the pages dealing with Dr. Reed's work at the Johns Hopkins Medical School.

Professor George M. Kober furnished the photograph of the bust of Dr. Reed by Hans Schuler.

There are other acknowledgments it would be pleasant to make, if space permitted.

Dr. Caroline Latimer has been my constant associate throughout, throwing herself into the work with an inspiring interest and zeal, without which it would never have been completed.

HOWARD A. KELLY

May, 1906

CONTENTS

CONTENTS

LIST OF ILLUSTRATIONS

WALTER REED AND YELLOW FEVER

CHAPTER I

BIRTH AND CHILDHOOD
1851-1876

When Nature has work to be done she creates a
genius to do it.—EMERSON.

WALTER REED, to whom the nineteenth century owed the last of her goodly array of scientific
discoveries, was born in Gloucester County, Virginia, September 13, 1851.

The Reed family were of English extraction,
being descended, as they suppose, from Sir Christopher Reed, of Chipchase Castle, on the Tyne. A
son of this Christopher was, at one time, Lord
Lieutenant of Ireland. Walter Reed's father,
Lemuel Sutton Reed, was a North Carolinian by
birth, though he passed nearly forty years of his
life in Virginia, as a minister of the Methodist
Church. His upright character together with his
mental endowments procured him distinction in
his profession, and he was for many years a
member of the Bishop's Council. His first wife,
Walter's mother, was Pharaba White, the daughter of a North Carolina planter, who also came of
a good English family. She was a loving, loyal-

prisoners, and were, therefore, released, but not until their families had been greatly alarmed by reports of their seizure. The horses, of course, were gone forever.

In 1866 the Reed family moved to Charlottesville, and there Walter, now fifteen years of age, was sent to a private school kept by a Mr. Abbott, a graduate of the University of Virginia. His education had been carried on without interruption up to this time, except for one year during the Civil War, when all the schools in his neighbourhood were closed, and he was well advanced for his age, especially in history and literature; but, strange to say, he does not seem to have shown any marked aptitude or taste for science during his boyhood. He remained with Mr. Abbott for two sessions and then entered the university, by special dispensation, as he was only sixteen, which was under the required age. Notwithstanding his extreme youth, his work was always good and he held a high place in all his classes. It was his earnest wish to go through the university, but as two of his brothers were already studying there with that intention, and his father's means were limited, he soon realised that it would be impossible for him to take the entire course. He applied, therefore, in person to the faculty to be certificated in the studies he had pursued, but this request was refused on the ground that he was under age. He then inquired whether he would be allowed to take the degree of doctor of medicine if he could pass the examinations. To this the faculty silently assented, thinking (as one of them afterwards told Reed's brother) that it was a safe promise, for the undertaking was an impossibility. Reed then turned to Dr. Maupin, the chairman, and said, "Doctor, you have heard what these gentlemen say. Will you see that I have my degree as M. D. if I make the required standard?" Dr. Maupin replied that he would, and Reed, bowing to the faculty, said, "Gentlemen, I hold you to your promise," and left the room. The friend who related this incident to Christopher Reed said that Walter's self-restraint and dignity, remarkable in a boy of sixteen, made a marked impression on those who were present.

Reed at once began his medical studies and graduated nine months later, in the summer of 1869, standing third in his class. Dr. Maupin, in presenting him his diploma, said that he was the youngest student ever graduated from the Medical School at Charlottesville, but that as he had fulfilled every requirement, the faculty were bound in honour to give him his degree.

Dr. A. R. Buckmaster, recently professor of obstetrics and practical medicine at the University

in sackcloth and ashes." Then, kneeling down by the bedside, he repeated the Lord's Prayer slowly and with deep emotion. Christopher Reed gave no sign of observing what passed, and the incident was never mentioned between the brothers.

While at one of the Brooklyn hospitals Dr. Reed attracted the attention of Dr. Joseph C. Hutchison, then the leading physician and surgeon of Brooklyn, and through his influence was appointed one of the five inspectors on the Brooklyn Board of Health. At this time Reed was only twenty-two years of age, but he had already established his reputation as a young man of the highest talents, especially distinguished for his skill in surgery. When on the Board of Health he came home one day greatly depressed, and on his brother's asking the reason, he replied, "To-day an elegant equipage with coachman and footman stopped in front of my office and a finely dressed gentleman came in, introducing himself as Dr. ———, and saying that he wished to report the death of a child. He was so grossly ignorant that he could not use medical nomenclature correctly, nor even state symptoms. I then asked him if he did not think it was such a disease [using the Latin term], and he answered 'Yes,' repeating the word backward. Yet this man has the leading practice in this part of Brooklyn, although he is

WALTER REED IN 1874

From a photograph taken in Murfreesboro, N. C.   Ætat 23

a first-class quack. I am disgusted and I should like to give up my profession."

In June, 1874, Dr. Reed paid a visit to his father, who was then living in the little town of Murfreesboro, in North Carolina. Walter's mother had died when he was a boy, and his father was now married again to a Mrs. Kyle, formerly Miss Mary Byrd, of Harrisonburg, Virginia. There was only one child of this second marriage, a daughter Annie, now Mrs. D. T. Elam of Farmville, Virginia.

It was during this visit to Murfreesboro that Dr. Reed made the acquaintance of his future wife, Miss Emilie Lawrence. Miss Lawrence's father, John Vaughan Lawrence, was a North Carolina planter of means and influence; he was descended from an English John Lawrence, who came to this country from the west of England in 1636 and settled in Watertown, Massachusetts. Her mother, Hannah Rea, belonged to another good old English family, which settled in Salem, Massachusetts, in 1630.

On Dr. Reed's return to New York he began a correspondence with Miss Lawrence, which affords an interesting insight into his thoughts and actions at this period of his life. It was during this year, 1874, that he made up his mind to give up the idea of general practice and to enter the army as a surgeon. His reasons for this determination, as given to his brother, were that success in general practice depended largely on social connection, the possession of wealth, and influential friends; and that as he was unable to rely upon these sources for advancement, he believed he had better take up a line where his future was secure and he could pursue scientific research. Long afterward, however, he admitted to his wife that his resolution to abandon general practice and enter the army arose from his desire to possess an assured competency as soon as possible in order that he might feel justified in asking her to marry him, and, indeed, anyone who reads the following letter, which was one of the earliest he wrote her, will see plainly how much he was actuated by this motive.

BROOKLYN, July 18, 1874.

I have been recently contemplating a departure from Brooklyn. My friends will consider me unwise in this, perhaps, but after due attention given to the matter I believe I will be justified in so doing. I have about made up my mind to make a strenuous effort to enter the Medical Corps of the United States Army. The Examining Board, which has not met before in six (6) years, assembles in New York City, August 4, next. I should not desire to remain longer than 3 or 4 years at the outside. And now for reasons. In the first place, the Board of Health are requiring more work of the Inspectors every day and to such a degree that the idea of private practice cannot be thought of —in fact they desire that the whole of an Inspector's time be devoted to the interest of the Health of his District. This is, doubtless, right enough in a strict interpretation, but it is such a " new departure " that I for one, fail to appreciate it. Secondly, these great cities have lost the fascination which formerly held me so fast. Four years ago, I would have remained here " though the heavens fall." I gave my hopes and ambitions a free rein and applied the whip and spur unsparingly. To live in any other place than New York or Brooklyn never entered my head, and if a person had advised me to go to some small town, I would have certified to his insanity. To such an extent does our folly mislead us! But since then a few more springs have come and gone, and though no grey hairs adorn my head, I have become a little wiser, I hope. I have carefully noted the success or failure of those around me and I have watched them in their sorrows and joys. Yet, during this time I have been unable to discover the great advantages of living in Metropolitan cities, except it be in the " wear and tear." It is true I never worked harder, but I can't say that it has brought me an equal amount of comfort. I have still a third reason. Having entered my profession about 4 years earlier than is the custom, I have experienced all the troubles of a youthful aspirant for honours. As long as my success depended upon actual knowledge and experience, I managed to overcome all obstacles, but the moment that I entered upon the race of life I at once found out the disadvantages of a youthful appearance. It is a remarkable fact that a man's success during the first decade depends more upon his beard than his brains. And inasmuch as I could boast of none of the former, and but an infinitesimal quantity of the latter, I found "Jordan to be a hard road to travel." Yet, notwithstanding these many drawbacks, my success has been greater than I expected, and unless I can obtain the sanction of home-folks, I will not leave. My stay in these cities has done me an incomparable good. By it I have obtained an extensive hospital and sanitary experience which is worth to me more than I can now estimate. It has also given me a truer insight into human nature than I would have acquired in an equal number of years elsewhere, while it has added to my respect for truth and morality. So that I count myself more than fortunate so far. On the other hand, I had thought that as I have no anxiety to plunge at once into the cares of life, a few years spent in travelling from one part of the country to another would be of profit to me. Of course all depends upon my ability to pass the examination, which is a very rigid one (I must confess I dread it). If at the end of that time (3 or 4 years hence) I could find some fair damsel who was foolish enough to trust me, I think I would get——married, and settle down to sober work for the rest of my days in some small city where one could enjoy the advantages of a city and at the same time not feel as if lost. For in what does life consist? What is its true philosophy? Is it to win the applause of the rabble, or to sit in high places? Do we not arrive nearer to true happiness in striving to accept what Divine Wisdom allots to us——doing all we can to assist our fellowmen in being happy and submitting uncomplainingly to the will of Him who gave us breath and life? Ever remembering that " he that humbleth himself shall be exalted."

Reed's resolution once taken, he began immediately to prepare for the necessary examination with characteristic thoroughness. A few years spent in active life without systematic application to study always renders the resumption of it difficult, and Reed's case was no exception. He writes about the examination to Miss Lawrence as follows:

BROOKLYN, Aug. 12, 1874.

If I appear amazingly stupid as I proceed, please remember that my mind has been racked during the past day or two with the " atomic theory " and the " law of equivalents " so that peradventure whatsoever I shall write will not contain one atom of news or be equivalent to your loss of time in reading it. From early morning till far into the hours of the night I must needs be plodding along through dry dusty details and charging my memory with a thousand items which may possibly prove useful to me in the coming ordeal. The truth is I was not aware of how much I had forgotten and in how many places the rust had accumulated till I began a careful review. The more I read, the greater the task looms up before me till I stand appalled at the work that must be done, and almost think all I ever knew has forsaken me. But one thing I will not permit to forsake me is my courage, and if effort will avail anything, it shall not fail me in this case. I went over to New York a few days ago and had a long talk with the Recorder of the Examining Board. To my utter astonishment he informed me that candidates must stand an examination in Latin, Greek, mathematics, and history, in addition to medical subjects. Horror of Horrors! Imagine me conjugating an irregular verb, or telling what $x+y$ equals, or what year Rome was founded, or the battle of Marathon fought. Why the thing is impossible, I shall utterly fail. Add to this that each applicant is examined five hours each day for six successive days—thirty hours' questioning —and, to cap the climax, there are more than 500 applicants for less than 30 vacancies? The very thought of it makes me dizzy. Think of my condition and pity me, for I need all the sympathy of all my friends.

The strain of such close application soon told upon Reed's health and spirits. He became much depressed, and about a month later he writes:

BROOKLYN, Sept. 17, 1874.

I owe you an apology for my long delay in answering your last letter. I would have written you promptly had I not been debarred from doing so by severe sickness. During three long weeks I have been confined to my room and during the greater part of this time I was scarcely able to raise my head from the pillow. Hence I have, of necessity, been compelled to forego executing many plans which I had projected, no one of which gave me more reason for regret than my inability to write to you. Doubtless my own folly was the cause of my indisposition. I had been trying to do more than my strength could bear. It may be

that I cannot do as much brainwork in the same length
of time as I could do in my younger days; or, perhaps,
a more correct statement would be that I have for so
long a time abandoned the habit of hard, continuous
application as to make it somewhat difficult, if not a
matter attended with danger, to return into the traces
quickly. I remember the time when I could safely study
as much as 20 hours uninterruptedly day after day,
and not experience any bad effect from it, but I presume
that time shall return no more. . . . But, really,
there is a charm in study which I fain must acknowledge.
Let me become interested with what the author is saying, and it is a difficult matter to break the spell, nor do
I cease to toil until my weary senses warn me that nature
is well-nigh exhausted. . . . Perhaps I decide to
dash aside the book and for once yield to refreshing
sleep, but quicker than ever winged lightning cleaved
heaven's vault the thought flashes through my mind
that there are a thousand things in that cast-aside volume of which I am ignorant, a thousand unanswerable
questions that may rise up against me in the day of my
examination, to humble and mortify me. Wracked with
a thousand fears, I tear open the book and eagerly scan
its pages, determined to exhaust every effort, and, if
need be, to suffer death rather than defeat. This is
what I have done and the result is sickness and mental
paralysis, and it is what I shall not dare to repeat. Too
happy in having regained my strength, I will see to it
that I do not precipitate myself into my former unhappy
condition. This I can do the more easily as I have now
abundance of time in which to review my studies. A few
days ago I received a notice from the Pres. Army Exam-

ination Board that I would not have to stand my examination till January 18th, 1875. Of course this suits me exactly."

In spite of the relief afforded by the postponement of his examination, Reed continued, as his letters show, to be much oppressed by his work, and he writes again two months later:

BROOKLYN, Nov. 3rd, 1874.

My second excuse for not writing is but a repetition of the same old story—ill-health. Alas! I am so harassed. What to do surpasses the infinite of thought. I must study—not a moment to lose—and it is this same studying that has all along delayed my convalescence. Sick! Why, I haven't drawn an unsound breath for years. But now, when I need all my strength, lo! it fails me. . . . Still I believe that when a person determines to accomplish an end, that he should put forth all honest effort, nor turn aside, unless for the best of reasons; and if he meets with defeat let him accept it like a man, remembering that many better men have found themselves in a like situation. At all events I shall pursue my course until every prop is knocked away from under me. Sufficient to the day is the evil thereof.

The morbid dread of failure arising from bodily weakness passed away as health returned, and in January, 1875, Reed writes cheerfully of his prospects. A month later, in February, 1875, after a second postponement, he passed his examinations brilliantly, and this event was shortly followed by his engagement to Miss Lawrence. In the following June he received his commission as Assistant Surgeon, with the rank of First Lieutenant.

His first station was Willet's Point, New York harbour, whence he writes to Miss Lawrence as follows:

WILLET'S POINT, Sept. 15, 1875.

Would you, could you believe that I would allow my twenty-fifth birthday to pass without so much as thinking of it during the whole day. The very day on which I wrote you last I was twenty-four years old (just think of it), and yet I was totally ignorant of it. Of course I felt the weight of years more than usual on that day, but I could not account for it. Suddenly on Tuesday the 14, it occurred to me that I was one year older and immediately the cause of my fatigue flashed across my mind. It is too late for me to grow eloquent over the subject (for I had intended to say something suitable to such an occasion), since the champagne has lost its effervescence, but still I can not permit my birth· day to pass without some remarks.

Alas, my twenty-fifth birthday has passed and what have I to show for it! What good deeds have I done that merit approbation! How negligent and wayward I have been! What golden moments of opportunity have come and gone, all unheeded! As I look back over my past life to-night, but few thoughts occur to me such as cause my bosom to swell with

to him. To postpone his marriage indefinitely was
not to be thought of, yet he could not bear to take
a young wife out to a rough, semi-civilised country with which he was not even himself familiar.
He decided to seek an interview with the Surgeon-
General and to find out whether, if he went to Arizona at the time appointed, he would be able to
obtain leave in the course of a few months to
return for his marriage. This was a step that required all his courage, for to a lieutenant in the
Army Medical Corps his chief is an all-power-
ful being, holding his subordinates entirely in his
power, and able to exalt or debase them at his
will. There was no help for it, however, and
Reed went to Washington.

His heart sank within him when he was ushered
into the presence, and after introducing himself,
was ordered in a peremptory manner to "Sit
down." Next came the abrupt question, "What
do you want?" "I would like to know, General,
if I can get a leave while I am in Arizona. I am
engaged to be married and should want to return." The General's voice became gruffer still
and his face more stern as he replied, "Young
man, if you don't want to go to Arizona, resign
from the service." At this Reed's spirit returned,
he lost all timidity, and answered fearlessly as
man to man, "General, I did not labour for my

commission with all the will which I did to throw it away hastily, nor can you deprive me of it till I act so unworthily as to cause dismissal." The old man's manner changed at once. He was evidently pleased by his young subordinate's spirit, and he answered kindly, " Have a cigar, Dr. Reed, and let us talk it over." At the end of the interview, he gave his ultimatum thus: " Don't marry now. Go to Arizona. There is no doubt some officer will become insane before long. You can bring him East, and there will be the chance for your wedding." In after years Dr. Reed often laughed at the patience he would have been called upon to exercise if he had followed the Surgeon-General's advice, for he had been married thirteen years before he was ordered to Washington to escort an officer to St. Elizabeth's Asylum.

As no change in the situation could be hoped for, the arrangements for the wedding were hastened, and it took place on April 25, 1876. Two weeks later Dr. Reed went to his command alone, wishing to ascertain what hardships would have to be faced, and also what arrangements could be made for his wife's comfort before she joined him.

CHAPTER II

FRONTIER LIFE
1876-1889

Es bildet ein Talent sich in der Stille.
—GOETHE.

IN May, 1876, Dr. Reed went to his post in Arizona, there to continue a garrison life which lasted eighteen years, the greater part of it being spent in the Far West.

In the following October his wife set forth from Norfolk, Virginia, to join him. At that time, when facilities for travel were not what they are now, such a journey was a great undertaking for a girl of twenty, who had never travelled alone for any distance before. Mrs. Reed's courage was, moreover, tried by several emergencies, such as a blizzard and a collision with a westward bound train. At the end of a week, however, she reached San Francisco, where Dr. Reed joined her, and they started for Fort Lowell, Arizona, a journey of twenty-two days, in an army waggon over the roughest kind of roads, and among the most primitive conditions. Some idea of the difficulties which beset their way may be formed from the following extract taken from a letter from Dr. Reed to his wife's sister, Mrs. J. N. Harrell:

We left San Diego, November 15, '76, at 2 P. M. My waggon, loaded with our baggage, had left at 1 P. M. I had been told, on careful inquiry, that the distance to the first station was 16 to 20 miles, which being the case, my waggon should have made it by 6 P. M. and my ambulance by 5 P. M. But " the best laid plans of mice," etc., etc. I soon found that the road was horribly rough and by 5 P. M. I had not made more than 10 miles, for I had to walk my team every step. By this time the sun was set and as there was no moon, it soon became so very dark that we could barely keep to the road. I had already overtaken and passed my waggon. By seven o'clock P. M. it had turned quite cold. I had Emilie put on her waterproof; I also had two overcoats, one of which I wrapped her feet snugly in and the other I had her put on, so that she was thoroughly prepared for the cold. I then told the driver to go very carefully, and to watch for any lights, so that we would be certain not to pass the station in the dark, for I thought it must be near by. On we went, keeping a good watch on each side, till my watch marked 9 P. M., and still no station. Emilie began to ask " How much further have we got to go? " quite frequently, and I could only answer, " It can't be far." A few minutes later and we espied a light ahead and to the right of our road. I now told Emilie to pluck up her courage as we should soon reach the station. However, when we had gone about half a mile, we found that the road left the light to our right, and hence I was much perplexed to know whether it was the station or not. I told the driver to go over and ascertain. He returned in about 20 minutes and stated that it was *not* the station! He said that the owner was very anxious that we should stay over night with him, although his accommodations were not the best in the world. He had neither hay nor grain for my animals; in fact, he could not furnish us even a bed to sleep in, inasmuch as he and his old lady had had a " family jar " on that very day, which had ended in the old lady walking off with the bed and bedding and leaving him the house. I could but feel extremely grateful to this gentleman for his kind proffer, but nevertheless concluded to decline his hospitality till some future day.

Our search thus fruitlessly terminated, we again began our weary march, Emilie, in the meantime, letting fall several *very small tears*. Bless her darling heart! I must give her credit for great bravery on this, her first night in an ambulance. I'm afraid, if there had been a stone wall near by *I* should have brought my head in violent contact with it. But there was nothing to be done but to go on. On, on, we plodded, so slow, so slow, for it was very dark and the road *horribly* rough. Several times it seemed as if the vehicle would certainly upset; several times the driver had to descend from his seat in order to find the road. Ten o'clock came, but no station or any sign of one! I had just examined my watch and found it 11 o'clock, when on making a short curve in the road, we saw a smouldering fire but a short distance ahead. On reaching it, we found that it was a small camp of two waggons. I got out and awoke one of the sleepers (there were two of them), who sat up in his bed, but

was not very communicative. He told me that the
station was about two miles further, but added, " over
the worst road in California." I thanked him for this
cheering intelligence, and was about to go on, when he
told me that the last mile was through a very bad
cañon, and then lying down and pulling the bed-cloth-
ing closely around him, he remarked to his companion,
" He'll have a devil of a time getting through that
cañon to-night! " which put me into such a good frame
of mind that I gave the order, at once, " go ahead."

One mile and we had reached the mouth of this
cañon, and as we proceeded, step by step, the hills
arose on either side high and dark. If before it had
been dark, it was now the very *blackness* of *darkness*.
The trees overhead cut off every ray of light. The
mules seemed disinclined to venture on, even under the
lash, and it began to look as if further progress was
impossible. I got out to take a look, but all I could
find out was that we were in the midst of rocks and
deep sand and no sign of a road! What was to be
done? Fortunately the driver had a lantern and a part
of a candle. This we lit, and taking with me a soldier
who was riding with the driver, I started ahead to
show the way. By keeping just in front of the team
and holloaing " Now to the right," " Now to the left,"
and " Now straight ahead," we managed to make some
progress. Poor E. all this time was in the ambulance
alone, and calling out continually, " Where are you, Dr.
Reed? Please come back and let the soldier carry the
lantern," but I told her I could trust no man living to
point the way out of this horrible cañon; and on I
went in sand nearly up to my knees, calling to the
driver all the time what course he should take. Not-

withstanding the very great advantage the lantern afforded and that I had an excellent driver, every fifty
yards would find a wheel stopped by some great
boulder. Oh! the terrible difficulties of that night! But
everything must have an ending, and after we had been
working like beavers for an hour, success at last crowned
our efforts. We had passed the cañon and reached the
station! (12.30 A. M.) Ah! I should like to tell you
what a sigh of relief escaped my breast and how happy
I felt when I saw the little house by the wayside. . . .
I soon aroused the station-keeper, who was a very
rough-looking specimen of a frontiersman, but under
all this roughness he concealed a kind heart, as you
will see.

But let me describe the station, called "Jamul"
(pronounced "Harmool"). It consisted of a small
house about 10 feet square, and a horse stable. The
keeper's residence (the same house above mentioned)
was constructed of plain boards, with spaces of half
an inch between the boards, possibly for ventilation,
as the window was very small. A dirt roof and dirt
floor. A piece of canvas stretched on a frame, which
he called his "bed," a small stool, a broken chair, a pine
table and a cooking stove completed the furniture.
Now to show you the kind heart that this rough fellow
had, he no sooner found that I had my wife with me
than he not only made a roaring fire, prepared us both
a nice cup of hot tea (which with the lunch that we
had, enabled us to make a good meal), but he also
abandoned his "bed" for us, himself sleeping for the
rest of the night in the stable! and for this kindness
he not only did not charge a penny, but he would not
take a cent although I insisted upon paying him! As

soon as Emilie got within doors and saw the bright
fire, her spirits rose accordingly, and when the tea
was ready and we each had our cup, her humour was
of the best. All her sprightliness returned and as she
took a glance around the room and saw the various
articles, she laughed heartily, and declared that she
wouldn't take anything for this experience. We talked
of homefolks and wished that they could see us just
as we were. The " bed " was especially an object of
much merriment to Emilie. She declared that she
could never rest on such a contrivance; but when I had
arranged things a little, had spread over the piece of
canvas a blanket which I found in the room and had
drawn my overcoats over us, we both soon fell asleep
and did not wake till broad daylight. Thus passed
Emilie's first day and night on her trip to Camp
Lowell! . . .

Fortunately both Dr. Reed and his wife possessed a keen sense of humour, which helped them
over many of their hardest experiences. The following anecdote told me by Mrs. Reed shows how
valuable a sense of the ludicrous was among such
surroundings.

Late one evening they drove up to a little shanty
perched on the side of the mountain, where the
country was so barren that there was not earth
enough to drive their tent pegs, and they were
forced to seek shelter for the night in the hut. Dr.
Reed had stopped at this place on his way to San
Francisco, and when he alighted he expected to find

the same friendly owner with whom he had made acquaintance three weeks before. To his surprise an entire stranger appeared, who told him that when roaming over the prairie a week or two before, he had come across this hut uninhabited, while the body of the former owner lay outside with a bullet through his heart. When Dr. Reed asked whether they could have accommodation for the night, the man replied in the affirmative, but said, referring to the previous owner, " The kyotes [coyotes] have about finished him, and I hope the young lady will not be afeared of his arm bone. I use it to prop open the window." And there, sure enough, was the bone in the window just over the spot where the visitors were expected to sleep!

Thirty years ago Arizona seemed as remote from civilisation as the Philippines do now. Communication with the East was imperfect and irregular; at one time when Dr. Reed was stationed at Camp Apache, he was seven hundred miles from a railroad, the mail arrived only once a week, and letters from the East were often six weeks on the way. Life at these distant posts was always hard and often desolate, nor was the element of danger absent. Dr. Reed, it is true, was never in the field, but the unsettled condition of the country and the presence of hostile Indians were a

WALTER REED IN 1876

From a photograph taken in Harrisonburg, Va.   Ætat 25

constant source of peril. On one occasion, when moving from Camp Lowell to Camp Apache, a journey of eleven days, Reed and his wife, with an escort of two soldiers, camped for the night on a quiet plain, which three days later was the battle-ground between two hostile tribes, who engaged in a bloody fight and left the peaceful spot a scene of frightful carnage. At another time when Dr. Reed had been relieved and was hastening to join his wife and child, a brother officer urged him to break the journey by stopping at his post, which was on the stage route, and Dr. Reed would have complied had it not been for his strong desire to join his wife without delay. He often said that his eagerness to push forward saved him from imminent peril and perhaps death, for the stage on which he would have travelled had he been a day later, as suggested, was waylaid by the Navajoes and the driver killed.

In the summer of 1877, after a year spent at Fort Lowell, Dr. Reed was transferred to Fort Apache, a journey which he and Mrs. Reed again performed in true frontier fashion. He himself gives a most graphic description of the difficulties which they encountered to his sister-in-law, Mrs. Harrell, and the account is so full of interest and of colour that I give the letter almost in full:

CAMP APACHE, ARIZONA,
October 25, 1877.

In this territory, as, in fact, in all others, officers
of the army, especially those who are married, travel
by ambulance whenever they can get one. Now I
know the word ambulance will at once recall to your
mind a long, black, funereal-looking vehicle, such as
you probably saw during the war. These army ambu-
lances, however, are constructed on the same pattern
as the ordinary stage, only a little smaller, have two
seats capable of seating four, and are drawn by four
to six mules. They are painted white so as to absorb
the terrible heat of the climate as little as possible. Such a vehicle you would have seen standing in
front of our quarters at Camp Lowell at nine o'clock
on the morning of August 11th last. The waggon
containing our baggage, to the extent of 1700 lbs.,
had started for Apache on the morning of the 10th,
so that we had but few things to put in the ambulance.
I will enumerate its contents as it stood ready for the
word to be given, " go ahead." *Inside* of the vehicle
there were the following articles: *On* the back seat,
Emilie, the dog Undina, and myself; *under* the back
seat, a box of medicines for emergencies, a lunch
basket, a jar of preserved ginger, a pair of boots, a
blacking brush, a bag containing a saucepan, frying
pan, tin pan, and coffee pot. *On* the front seat, two
folding chairs, my valise, Emilie's companion, a basket
containing her work, a bundle of shawls, my overcoat,
two double blankets, a feather pillow, a clothes brush,
and four books of light literature; *under* the front seat,
a mess-chest containing the necessary tableware for the
journey, a box of provisions, and a large clothes basket

containing everything from a hairpin to a pair of shoes. Suspended from various points of the roof were two hats, a sword, an umbrella, a pair of E.'s shoes, a carbine, a pistol, a belt full of cartridges, and two canteens filled with water. Now for the outside: *underneath* the driver's seat in front were my private case of instruments weighing 50 lbs., a sack of grain, and the driver's rations for ten days; *on* the seat behind, my trunk, and bedding consisting of a mattress, blankets, sheets, etc., done up in a canvas cover. There may have escaped my memory a few articles, but I believe I have mentioned all. If there was anything on top I did not see it. I have a lurking idea, however, that the driver concealed several chairs and boxes in odd places about the vehicle. I forgot to say that beside the driver there was a corporal on the seat with him, a very light man, weighing just two hundred lbs.

Thus equipped, after bidding good-bye to our Lowell friends, we started for Camp Apache, external temperature 110°. As Undina had never before ridden in a vehicle, she straightway set up a terrific barking, which she kept up till she was so hoarse that she couldn't hear herself, and then stopped. Our destination for the first day was *" Tres Alimos "* or " The Three Cottonwoods," a small settlement 40 miles from Lowell. Aside from the heat, the day was not an unpleasant one for travelling. We passed our time in chatting and laughing at Undina's queer freaks (who, by the way, wasn't quiet in any one place for a minute at a time) till it was time for taking lunch. Perhaps you have never taken what is called a " flying lunch." If not, let me tell you, you have missed a *great deal of fun.* Mind you, everything connected with the meal is done while the ambulance is in full progress—no stopping "five minutes for refreshments," and as the road is most often very rough and rocky, and always so when you think it is about time to eat, and as the driver concludes to whip his horses up to their very best speed just at this time, whereas he had been persistently permitting them to walk for the last hour, why, the feat of getting anything into your mouth becomes a matter of considerable uncertainty. . . . It is needless for me to narrate at length all the trials of this meal; I could not, however, forbear showing you what you have missed by never partaking of a "flying lunch."

At sunset we reached our destination, *"Tres Alimos."* When I had got Emilie into a very comfortable and well-furnished room, I proceeded to unpack all those articles enumerated in the beginning of my letter, and when you take into consideration the fact that I had to unpack all of them every night and put them back every morning, you will know that it was quite a task. I would have had one of the men do the packing for me, but it would have taken so long to teach him, for every article had to go in a certain place and nowhere else, that I thought it would be easier to do it myself. At 7 o'clock we had a very nice supper, consisting of fried spring chicken, good milk, butter, etc., and after I had seen about a lunch for the morrow, we retired, for we were to start the next morning at 4 o'clock, so as to reach the next station, 30 miles distant, before noon and thus avoid the heat of the afternoon. . . .

At the aforesaid hour we were up and preparing

for our journey. A cup of tea and everything stowed
away safely in the ambulance, not forgetting the little
dog, and we were ready for our day's trip. This day
we had to pass what are called the "Lime Kilns," a
place where Indians (I mean hostile ones) have been
often seen, and I must confess that I felt the least bit
anxious. However, I said nothing to E. about it, but
took good care to have all my weapons loaded and
in good reach and kept my eyes well open. When I
imagined that we were pretty near the "Kilns" I
called to the driver and told him to let me know when
he got there, whereupon, much to my satisfaction, he
replied that we had already passed them. A ride of
15 miles further and we had reached our station, called
"The Point of the Mountain"; so named from the
fact of the station being situated just where a mountain
range abruptly ends on the plain. Looking across a
plain, 20 miles in width, we can see the "Chiricahua
Mountains," well known in Arizona history as the
home of the celebrated Indian Chief "Cochise" and
his Chiricahua tribe, Indians that have killed more
people in Arizona than all the other tribes put together. We can follow with the eye the plain, white
stage road as it stretches across the intervening country and see it where it enters the mountains. Could
the eye but follow it 4 miles further, we should see
the spot where three mail-riders have recently fallen,
pierced by the bullets of the savages. The last one was
killed just a week before we commenced our journey.
This night, as we had very good accommodations,
we rested very well and awoke much refreshed. You
would think it rather fatiguing, I guess, to have to
ride 70 miles in two days. But there's nothing like

tween Camp Thomas and Camp Apache. We arrived in camp about 3 P. M. Soon afterwards I saw an Indian on a hill opposite camp. He came over, sat down by the side of me, and laying down his gun, said "*El campo Apache*," by which I knew that he was going to Apache. A minute later he said "*pan*," at which I wasn't surprised, for they are always ready to eat. I gave him a loaf that was as dry as ashes and as hard as a " nigger's head," and the way he demolished it was astonishing. Having filled his stomach, he picked up his gun, said "*adios*," and a moment later was lost to sight. When I got to Apache our recognition was mutual. The Indian turned out to be the celebrated " Dead-shot," so named because he never misses his game, whether man or otherwise. We had our supper under the " umbrageous foliage " of a cedar tree and about 6.30 P. M. prepared to retire. We had no tent, but slept in the ambulance. The seats were so constructed that they could be slid together, forming a perfect floor. On this came our bedding and when we had made the curtains fast and tight, we were ready for hail or rain. Little Undina each night found a warm bed at our feet.

We broke camp Saturday morning about 8 o'clock, as we only had 12 miles to go in order to reach water, for you must remember that in Arizona the length of a day's travel depends upon the distance between watering places. There are no streams every few miles, as in the East. Sometimes you go forty or even sixty miles without seeing a drop of water, and you rarely have to travel less than 30 miles. " Ash Creek," our camp this day, was reached by noon. I made a heroic effort to catch some fish here, but after broiling in the sun an hour I only got one bite and that proved to be a plaguey turtle, to get which off my hook consumed another hour. I gave up fishing in disgust. " Ash Creek " is worth mentioning for this reason: about the time our dinner was well under way a terrific rainstorm came up, and as our bake-oven had no top our bread was soon afloat and the poor soldier, our cook, looked as if he had lost his best friend; but it was no use to try to make anything out of that bread, for it was so soaked that it weighed a pound to the square inch.

We left our camp next morning bright and early, as we were this day to pass over the worst road in Arizona, yes, the worst road in the world. When we had gone about 4 miles we began to ascend very slowly and gradually the slope of the " White Mountains." Soon we entered what is called " Rocky Cañon " and no person who has been over this " Cañon " once will ever forget it. It is useless for me to attempt to describe this road to you. It is simply beyond language to describe its awful roughness. For a distance of about 3 miles the ambulance scarcely touches " *terra firma* "; the wheels jump from rock to rock with a perfect *crash* at times. But this is the *good* part of the road, I assure you. When we had gone over this, which required about 2 hours, we came to what is designated " Nautaumes Hill." This is about three-quarters of a mile long to the summit. Standing at the foot of the hill and casting your eye upwards, you see nothing but solid stone, broken and tossed into all manner of shapes and positions. You would declare that no such thing as a waggon could ever go up or come down without being smashed into a thousand fragments. Im-

all right; it is on this sole condition that I send it. Emilie joins me in love to all. Pardon my abrupt ending, write soon, and believe me very affectionately, your brother,   WALTER REED.

Camp Apache was at length reached in safety, and there the Reeds remained nearly four years, during which time their eldest child, Walter Lawrence Reed, was born, on December 4, 1878. Their life during these years was not lacking in the difficulties and privations with which existence on the frontier is always filled, but these were met by them in the brave and cheerful spirit which reduces all troubles to a minimum. The following letter from Dr. Reed to Mrs. Harrell gives an amusing account of one variety of annoyance with which he and his wife had to contend.

CAMP APACHE, ARIZONA,
April 14, 1878.

You know that in civilised life it is not allowable for an officer to have a soldier do his cooking, because he can easily get servants to do his work. But on the frontier, and especially in such a delectable country as " Arizony " where it is simply impossible to find hand-maidens, unless it be an occasional Chinaman, it is permitted to use soldiers as cooks, provided they are willing to cook. Of course it is at the option of the soldier whether he will do duty with his company or cook. I will premise by saying that nearly all soldiers can cook after a fashion, and some of them very well, but most of them have a dislike to cooking for a married officer. The " pig under the fence " is the officer's wife. Soldiers will take any order and any amount of abuse from an officer without murmuring, but when it comes to receiving orders or even suggestions from a lady, they rebel at once. . . . Another point to bear in mind is that soldiers, with but few exceptions, are very fond of their " toddy " and always get drunk after pay day, which comes every two months.

You will remember that up to December last we messed with Mrs. Colonel Andrews, and hence had no trouble about cooks. On the first of December, however, we went to housekeeping, for reasons which it is not necessary to state, being no less than the expected advent of a " kid," and so I had to look about for a soldier to do my cooking. After much search I lit upon one James Anmach, a high private in the rear rank. Now this same private Anmach is a considerable personage, having had no less than seven trades or professions, as follows: He is a natural born plasterer; in his early years he took up painting as a fine art; waxing stronger he devoted himself, his time and muscle to carpentering; finding that this occupation cramped his mental powers too much he turned his attention to brightening rusty knife blades and sharpening scissors, etc.; subsequently, circumstances over which he had no control forced him to become a plumber, for you know the greatest intellects must at times yield to the course of events; and finally, ruthless fortune converted him into a farmer. Now what he does not know about horses and cows is entirely superfluous knowledge. As an extractor of the " albine fluid " he has no equal. Indeed the cow herself is amazed at his dexterous performance. If the animal manifests any desire to run him through with her horns, he throws a lariat round the horns and fastens her head to a post; and then, if she makes too free with her posterior extremities, he simply ties them snugly together with a rope, and as he milks pays not the least attention to her frantic efforts to extricate herself.

Such an one was James Anmach, my new cook, on the first day of December, 1877. I should state that he knew nothing about cooking whatever, but as he expressed it " he would not mind learning to cook, as it might be useful to him one of these days." I presume the real reason was because he had so few trades. Upon his assumption of the culinary dignity I had a brief interview with Mr. Anmach, in which I expressed to him my earnest desire that he would abstain from all intoxicating liquors, for a time at least. After the birth of the future President I again told him that I hoped while Mrs. Reed was sick he would keep sober, for should he get on a spree and absent himself for a week or so, I would have no one to cook but myself and would be placed in a most deplorable position. He declared that should he *think* of getting drunk under the circumstances he would consider himself no better than a " dog " and that I might place full confidence in his sobriety.

Fortunately he turned out to be a very fair cook; a plain one, but he knew how to season food and could make pretty good bread and coffee, beside flannel cakes, etc. But he had the most curious ideas about crockery and its uses of any man I ever met. In the first place, he had a perfect mania for soup-plates. It made no difference what the dish was, whether beefsteak, chicken, tomatoes, corn, flannel cakes, or what not, he always brought it to table in a soup-plate and insisted on my eating out of the same kind of plate. I really believe he would have served the coffee in the same, if he could have found another one. Luckily we have only six soup-plates, and when he got these full he had to resort to something else. I gently remonstrated with him and pointed out the uses of a few utensils, but whether my explanations confused him or were too stupendous to grasp, I know not; I do know that the following day at dinner he fairly knocked the breath out of me by serving the tomatoes in the slop-bowl, the potatoes in the soup-tureen, and the pickles in the gravy-boat. I ate my dinner in silence, and from that day I never made any suggestions to Mr. Anmach. He took a great deal of pains in preparing his dishes, but when once cooked his mission ended, and he served them regardless of all traditions.

I cannot remember all the ingenious freaks of this man Anmach. On one occasion he served the soup in the cream pitcher, on another day on lifting the lid of the soup-tureen what should I find but half-a-dozen peach dumplings reposing therein. I think he intended this as a surprise, but I betrayed no astonishment whatever. He could not have told from my face but that I had been used to eating peach dumplings out of soup-tureens all my life. A few days after that when I attempted to fill my glass with water and found instead boiled potatoes in the pitcher, I may have betrayed some momentary surprise, but I think not. You may think I am falsifying, but I assure you that I am giving stern facts.

When I had lulled myself into the belief that private

Anmach would cling to his early training and keep sober, it came to pass that that season of the year drew nigh which has been so beautifully described by Lord Macauley in the words " Apple cider, cinnamon beer; Christmas comes but once a year." Perhaps the recollection of other days came back to him and led him astray, for at any rate Christmas night I heard a noise in Anmach's room about 11 o'clock and going in found him quite drunk and made him go to bed. I locked the door and put the key in my pocket, but to my surprise when I went to his room next morning about 7 o'clock, I found the bird had flown. I then went into the kitchen and found everything in confusion. As I stood there and cast my eye over the various frying-pans and tea-kettles, and especially the cold, ashy face of the old stove, I realised for the first time the true beauty of *soldier* cooks.

I returned and told the mother of the future President that our festive cook was gone, and took council with her as to how the dilemma was to be met. After a brief session of five minutes' duration, it was decided that I should peel off my jacket and approach the pensive frying-pan. I cannot say that I essayed the task with songs of joy upon my lips, but still I was determined that no one should cheat me out of my breakfast that morning. The bill of fare was as follows: *Pan frésco, mantéca, café caliente y huevos asados.* Now does not that sound like a city hotel? Reduced to plain English it is not quite so overpowering, but fresh bread, butter, hot coffee, and boiled eggs are at all times refreshing. For three days and nights I saw nothing of my truant cook, and during this time I got up various unspeakable and uneatable dishes. Emilie, however, lacked for nothing, for the ladies sent her meals regularly. On the morning of the fourth day a soft knock at the door announced the return of the wanderer. I had fully made up my mind to give him " rats," but he ate such a quantity of humble pie that I could say nothing. He acknowledged his meanness in leaving me under the circumstances, calling himself a good-for-nothing " dog " and promising never to deceive me again.

Everything now went on lovely, and as Emilie was out of bed by January 15 and able to direct affairs I had high hopes that we had passed the worst. Contrary to my advice, however, Emilie insisted that the vegetables should go into the vegetable dishes, the soup into the tureen, and a lot of other nonsensical ideas which I felt convinced our man Friday would never submit to. And sure enough, just four days thereafter, January 19th, the man of many trades slid off again, this time on a drunk as before, and again I was elected cook. After waiting five days and finding that cooking was a trifle monotonous I employed another cook, private George Powers, the " meek-eyed." He did very well, and as he was sober and learned willingly and quickly, Emilie was on the fair road to make him a first-class cook. But lo! there were breakers ahead! The Commanding Officer's cook got on a rampage and was sent back to his company. Hence the Commanding Officer (as private Powers belonged to his company) found himself under the " painful necessity " (which, by the way, was all painful fiddlesticks) of taking our cook to cook for his family. So on March 1st we had to let him go and take as our bread-maker one private Bertrand Howard, the sullen, and, I may add, the lazy. He had the reputation of being an excellent cook, and thought he knew everything. He could make excellent cakes for breakfast and pretty good pumpkin pies, but beyond this his cooking was a mess. He could not bear for Emilie to give him any suggestions, and as for her coming into the kitchen it made him very angry for a week. He thought he knew so much that he wouldn't follow any receipt and in fact just cooked after his own style and liking. As we had had so much trouble I begged Emilie to put up with him, although she could hardly help throwing a frying-pan at his head. Mr. Howard was much inclined to laziness, so that when we began to move to our new house and he found he would have to do a little extra work in cleaning the kitchen, he came to me and said he would like to go back to his company. I was so disgusted with the gentleman's performance that I paid him and told him to report at once. Thus blooming April found us once more minus a cook, and that too while we were busy moving. I tried various soldiers, but could get no one to come. In fact there seemed to be a perfect dearth of cooks, and I knew not what to do, when a happy thought occurred to us. What do you suppose it was? It was E.'s suggestion. To take back to our hearts our old friend the plasterer, alias the painter, alias the carpenter, alias the cutler, alias the tinner, alias the farmer, alias the cook, alias James Anmach of the Horse Marines!

And we did! We have the most beautiful contract drawn up imaginable, and it is as simple as it is beautiful. Private Anmach agrees to cook and do general work, such as milking, etc., to put the soup into its proper tureen, and not to put the potatoes in the water pitcher, provided he is permitted to have a week's drunk after each pay day, or once in two months. Once more the God of day has chased away the clouds and we are happy. I am glad to say that under E.'s skilful generalship he is doing amazingly, even going so far as to make a citron pudding after your latest receipt, which was mighty good and gave us indigestion like all the world.

And this is all I know about cooks in general and *soldier* cooks in particular. Best love to all, in which E. and baby join. Write soon.

Your affectionate brother,
WALTER REED.

P. S.—I am constrained to add a few lines which are so appropriate to the present occasion that I hope you will not consider me verbose.

> " *We may live without poetry, music, or art;*
> *We may live without conscience and live without heart;*
> *We may live without friends and live without books;*
> *But civilised man cannot live without cooks.*"

As a post surgeon Dr. Reed was greatly and deservedly beloved. At this time, as Dr. Walter D. McCaw says in his " Memoir of Walter Reed," the young medical officer at an army post was generally the only physician at the station, and was called upon by the settlers for miles around. Without help and with only such instruments and medicines as could be hastily stuffed into his saddle bags, he would be summoned to attend a fractured thigh, a child choking to death with diphtheria, or, most trying of all, a difficult childbirth. At one time when Dr. Reed himself was ill with a fever and cared for by the hospital steward, he insisted on responding to any urgent call, would get up, ill as he was, sit down repeatedly while dressing for lack of strength, and finally start out with the snow deep on the ground and the thermometer far below zero. It has more than once happened that on reaching the patient's house he would have to lie down and recover himself before he could go upstairs. The more humble the patient, the greater was Dr. Reed's devotion, for the impression made upon him by his experience among the poor in his New York district was never effaced, and his heart always went out to the lowly and the ignorant.

His devotion was especially strong to children, and often, if some little one's life was in danger from ignorance and want of proper care, he would plead with his wife to let it be brought to his home in order that his injunctions could be carried out, a plan which she was forced to oppose, as their home life would have been destroyed if their house had been turned into a hospital. On one occasion he brought into the camp a little Indian girl of four or five, so horribly burned that her people had left her to die. This child he succeeded in saving, and then brought her up in his own family as nurse to his children, in spite of a friendly warning from that keen old Indian fighter, General Crook. When this child was nearly a woman the savage Apache blood asserted itself and she ran away, after giving abundant evidence (so says Major Kean) that fifteen years of kindness, gentleness, and refinement had not modified the cruel and deceitful characteristics of her race.

The friendly Indians settled near the post often sent for Dr. Reed to prescribe for them, and he was as painstaking in their behalf as in that of any other patient, although he was well aware that the Medicine Man's word had much more weight than his own, and that as soon as he was gone the drum and rattle of the latter would be persistently beaten at the patient's bedside, even though he might have given a narcotic. The Indians, nevertheless, were much attached to him, and often showed their regard by bringing him a haunch of venison. If no one was in the house to receive it, they would walk in stealthily and lay it on Mrs. Reed's dressing table, or, perhaps, take a picture from the wall and hang the venison in its stead.

With all Dr. Reed's gentleness his sense of personal dignity and justice was strong and he never allowed anyone, even a superior officer, to infringe upon his rights, or to fail in treating him with the respect to which he was entitled. Several times during his garrison life he had reason to think that the commanding officer was usurping authority, and he at once appealed to the higher powers, knowing that he was in the right and that an un-biassed judgment would decide in his favour. Once, while a soldier was still on the sick list, the commanding officer saw him taking a walk and ordered him to duty, saying that if he was well enough to be out, he was well enough to work. Dr. Reed's anger was justly roused, but his temper was always under his control. Without al-lowing himself to speak, he sent a written com-munication through the commanding officer to Headquarters, asking whether such interference was allowed. The paper was promptly returned through the proper channels to the commanding officer, who read it and handed it to his adjutant to be forwarded to Dr. Reed, remarking, " D——the doctors, Mr. Adjutant, we can never get ahead of them."

Dr. Reed took the greatest interest in his army hospitals and in the hospital corps. His influence over his men was very great and he inspired them with his own enthusiasm, so that order and neat-ness prevailed wherever he ruled. Cleanliness is next to Godliness was his motto. Drinking he would not permit under any circumstances among the hospital attendants, and in subsequent years several of his former hospital stewards sought him out and thanked him for keeping them bound to a temperance pledge while in hospital service.

His love for outdoor sports was very strong, and a Western life afforded him opportunities of hunting, which he greatly enjoyed. In 1879 his wife went back East to spend a year at home, and he writes to her as follows concerning a deer hunt in which he had been engaged:

FORT APACHE, ARIZONA,
December 23, 1879.

My last letter was not a very long one for the reason that I was getting ready to go for a "big hunt" with Lieutenants Kingsbury and Cruse, although I did not mention it at the time. Well, we got away from the post about 8 o'clock on Wednesday morning, and away we hied to "Bonito Fork," the scene of our former hunting expedition, on which occasion the deer we killed and the turkey we slew would not have furnished fresh meat for many days. On this occasion, however, beside four soldiers and four packers, we had twenty of the Indian Company, so that when we arrived at our camp that afternoon we found four turkeys and a fine big deer awaiting us. . . . .
Our little camp looked real pretty at night. We were on the extreme right, then came our soldiers' camp about 30 feet away, then the packers', and farther still

the 20 Indians, divided into two camps of 10 each, so that there were five camp fires burning brightly and stretched along in a line about 30 feet apart. We had a good tent for ourselves and one for the soldiers. You should have seen our beds. Lieutenant Cruse and I dug a small hole on each side of the tent large enough to admit our backbones, and then filled both of them with long dry grass which we cut from the mountain side, thus making a delightfully soft cushion for our bones—a sort of hair mattress with springs, as it were, over which we spread our blankets. I slept with 4 blankets under me *doubled over,* and 8 over me with my night-cap and a good heavy comforter which Mrs. Harrison gave me around my neck, and I managed to exclude the cold pretty well. I forgot to say that I had Lieutenant Kingsbury's dog sleeping on my feet to keep them warm, and pretty cold it was too. Next morning (Thursday) when we got up, bright and early, we found about half an inch of snow on the ground and the wind was singing merrily through the trees. The Indians had already skipped out for a day's hunt, and while we ate our broiled venison for breakfast we now and then heard a sharp crack of a rifle, which we knew meant either a turkey or a deer. After breakfast was over (I am sorry to say that I did not wash my face that morning, it was *so* cold) Lieutenant Cruse and I took our guns and climbed a high hill which took the breath clean out of us and then away we went, tramping over the roughest country you almost ever saw, and we kept our walk till 2 P. M., but we didn't get anything, as the Indians were ahead of us and frightened all the game away. We got back at 2 P. M. to camp, and such a dinner as we two ate would

have supplied half a dozen hungry men. . . . By
the time we had finished the Indians began to come
in with their game, and before the sun had sunk beneath the western horizon we counted 13 deer and 10
turkeys as the result of one day's shooting. I attended
to "drawing" the turkeys, in fact, did it all myself,
and Lieutenant Kingsbury superintended cleaning the
deer. Before night we had them all hung up on a rope
stretched between two tall pines and by the light glim-
mer of the camp fire the display of game was very
fine. . . . . Next morning we were up before the
stars ceased shining, busy taking down our tent and
bundling up our baggage ready for a day's journey to
another branch of Black River, about 7 miles farther
away. We were there and in camp by 12 o'clock noon,
and after camp was pitched we lay off on our backs, and
snoozed and sang songs and had a jolly time generally.
That afternoon the Indians brought in 5 turkeys and
6 deer and reported that they had left hanging out in
the trees, from 5 to 15 miles away, 13 more big deer
so large that they couldn't pack them on their backs.
That night we had a glorious time broiling venison
over the red-hot coals. We ate and ate and yet did not
seem to have enough. We held a council of war that
night and decided to send in to the post next morning
16 deer and 17 turkeys as a gentle reminder to the
folks at Apache that we were as good hunters as other
people. After getting the party off to Apache early
next morning (Saturday) we started in various directions to get the deer that were hanging out. Sam Bow-
man and I went out with two pack mules, and after
travelling about 5 miles over mountains and cañons
we brought in 4 beautiful deer, but such a tramp as we

had. The Indian who went to show us where the deer were said that it was only " *poco logos* " that is " a little far " (Dandy-Bill, our old friend, by the way, was the *caballiero*), and I never knew what " *poco logos* " was before, but I know now. It means about 50 miles for a white man! I was so tired when I got back to camp that it took about 3 pounds of venison stew to refresh my drooping spirits! Saturday night it began to storm and rained all night, and continued so to do all day Sunday, so that no hunting could be done by the Indians. All day we lay in our tents with a roaring fire in front and did not have to go out, except for meals, which even the storm could not keep us from.
. . . . We concluded that night that our hunt was over, as the storm only increased in severity and we only waited for the return of the pack mules from Apache in order to pack up our duds and hie to the camp. They returned on Monday, too late for a start back on the same day. On Tuesday morning (yesterday), however, we started back again to Apache and faced a terrible storm till 2 P. M. . . . . In all we killed 41 deer and 50 turkeys! This morning we distributed the game and now everyone at the Post has enough fresh meat for their Christmas dinner. . . . A thousand Happy New Years for my sweet wife and son! God bless and preserve you both is ever the prayer of your fond and devoted husband,

WALTER OF ARIZONA.

At the end of four years in Arizona, Dr. Reed was ordered East again, being promoted at the same time to the rank of captain. In 1881 he was stationed for a short time at Fort McHenry, Baltimore, and while there made use of the opportunity to study physiology at the Johns Hopkins University. This work may really be considered his introduction to the world of modern scientific research, and it was during this period that he laid the foundations of his future distinction.

In 1882 Dr. Reed was transferred to the Department of the Platte and stationed in Western Nebraska. It was during the next year, while he was living at Fort Omaha, that his second child, Emilie Lawrence Reed, was born, on July 12, 1883.

While serving in Nebraska, Dr. Reed was frequently called on to practice among the poor settlers known as "Grangers," who eke out a wretched subsistence by trying to farm in a country where the rainfall is barely sufficient for a good crop once in three years. In the winters he was often obliged to take journeys on horseback in the discharge of his professional duties that were really dangerous from the risk of being overtaken by one of those blizzards in which the most experienced frontiersman cannot see his way and the staunchest horse turns tail, so that the lost traveller is in greater peril than he would be on a battlefield. A little incident occurred on one of these expeditions which Dr. Reed always referred to with amusement as an instance of the difference in man's " point of view."

He was sent for while a blizzard was raging and the thermometer was below zero, to go a distance of twelve miles to see a sick woman. He started at sunset in a driving wind, out on to the open prairie, where nothing could be seen but a sheet of snow, stretching miles and miles ahead of him, without a landmark visible. It was not long before he lost his way, and wandered about aimlessly until midnight, when suddenly, from behind a snowdrift, a little beacon of light appeared and he found the tiny cabin he was seeking. The woman was very ill, and he could not leave her till the next afternoon, during which time the husband did his best to entertain him. While they were sitting before a rickety three-legged stove, waiting for some coffee to boil, the old man drawled out, " Well, Doc, I often feels sorry for you folks at the post. I know you all must git powerful lonely sometimes." The post consisted of four companies, with headquarters and the band; moreover, it was situated within sight of the railroad station; and Dr. Reed, with the recollection of it in his mind, was at that very moment commiserating inwardly the utter isolation of this poor old pair in their remote cabin.

In 1887, after five years in Nebraska, Dr. Reed

WALTER REED IN 1882

From a photograph taken in Washington, D. C.   Ætat 31

was ordered to Mount Vernon Barracks, Alabama, and his delight in the change of surroundings was intense. After the barren desolation and trying climate of Nebraska, to say nothing of the still worse condition of things in Arizona, the sunshine, showers, and abundant vegetation of the South were a never-ending delight. His love for nature knew no bounds, and wherever he was stationed, even among the most untoward surroundings, he would manage to have a garden full of flowers for his friends and of fruit and vegetables for his hospital. It was a familiar sight to see him returning from an early morning visit laden with flowers gathered on his homeward way.

He had a great admiration for the magnolia tree, indigenous to southern Alabama, and once transplanted a couple of them into the hospital yard; shortly afterwards, a countryman, observing them, came to him and entreated that they might be uprooted, as it was a firm belief in that part of the country that if a transplanted tree lives, some member of the family owning it will die within the year. Dr. Reed, greatly amused, set to work immediately to scour the woods until he found a sufficient number of small magnolia trees to set out a whole row, saying that he would teach the country people a lesson. The trees lived, and no member of the family died, but it is not known whether the superstition survived or not.

In 1889 Dr. Reed began to feel keenly that he needed time and opportunity for study, in order to keep abreast of advances in medical research. He applied, therefore, for leave of absence, stating his reasons for doing so and the advantages to himself and to others that he hoped to gain from it. The reply from headquarters was that if he would pay the salary of a contract surgeon to fill his place he might go. This was a bitter disappointment, but fortunately it was only for a short time. The old order in Washington was just then giving place to new, and with the change sufficient interest was manifested in his application to insure his appointment as Attending Surgeon and Examiner of Recruits in Baltimore, with permission to pursue some line of professional work at the Johns Hopkins Hospital, at that time just opened to physicians for courses in clinical medicine, surgery, and laboratory work. Even then, however, he was not free to follow his own inclinations without restriction. He consulted the superintendent of the hospital as to his best line of work, and was advised to take courses in pathology and bacteriology in addition to certain clinical work in general medicine and surgery. Dr. Reed showed great interest in the suggestion, but answered with regret that the Surgeon-General had forbidden him to give any attention to laboratory work and had informed him, curtly and pointedly, that the object of the Government in detailing him for service in Baltimore was that he might better familiarise himself with the care of sick soldiers; under the circumstances, he felt that he could not, in honour, pursue any laboratory courses. He began his work, therefore, exclusively on the clinical side of the hospital, but fortunately for himself and for the country he was not obliged to remain there. Surgeon-General Baxter died suddenly a few weeks later, and the new Surgeon-General was much more in sympathy with scientific pursuits, so that after obtaining the necessary permission, Dr. Reed devoted himself largely to pathology and bacteriology, in which lines of work he soon became known as a worker of the utmost promise. The quiet years of practical work on the frontier had furnished an admirable soil for the development of his talents, and they were now ready to yield an abundant harvest.

CHAPTER III

BEGINNING OF SCIENTIFIC WORK
1890-1899

In all things sought to see the Whole,
  Brooked no disguise;
And set his heart upon the goal,
  Not on the prize.
      —WILLIAM WATSON, *Laleham Churchyard.*

THE winter of 1890-91 was one of the keenest enjoyment to Dr. Reed. After living for so many years at a distance from the scientific world and cut off from congenial companionship, he returned to both with delight. His work at the Johns Hopkins Hospital brought him into the society of cultivated, scientific men, with whom his own genial nature and charming manner made him universally popular. He made many warm friendships during this year of his life, among which he set special value on that of his beloved teacher, Professor William Welch.

The following account of Dr. Reed's work at the Johns Hopkins University and Hospital has been kindly supplied me by Dr. Welch:

Dr. Reed was sent to Baltimore in October, 1890, as Attending Surgeon and Examiner of Recruits, and he remained there until the following October. The Medical Department of the University was not opened until October, 1893, but the Hospital was in full operation in 1889, and the Pathological Laboratory of the Hospital and the University had been equipped and opened for the reception of physicians and advanced students and for research since 1885. Here systematic laboratory courses were given in pathology and bacteriology, and it was here that Dr. Reed received his fundamental training in these subjects.

Dr. Reed began his work on the clinical side of the Hospital, but after a few weeks, a new Surgeon-General having in the meantime been appointed, he was enabled to follow his own inclination and to enter the regular courses in pathology and bacteriology in the Pathological Laboratory. I well recall with what eagerness and enthusiasm he 'turned his attention to the new fields of scientific medicine thus first opened to him, which from that time until the end of his life became the centre of his professional interest and activity, and which he himself was destined to cultivate with such signal benefits to medical science and to the welfare of mankind.

The decade preceding the time when Dr. Reed began his practical studies at the Johns Hopkins had been a period of marvellous progress in our knowledge of infectious diseases. Upon the basis of the discoveries of Pasteur and of Koch, and particularly as a result of the new methods introduced by Koch for the cultivation and study of bacteria, there had followed in rapid succession within this period such important discoveries as those of the specific germs causing tuber-culosis, cholera, leprosy, glanders, erysipelas, surgical infections, tetanus, pneumonia, typhoid fever, malaria, amœbic dysentery, cerebro-spinal meningitis, diph-theria, and a large number of animal diseases. Pasteur had discovered methods of rendering animals arti-ficially immune from chicken-cholera and other dis-eases, and had devised his method of protective inoc-ulation against rabies, which has been the means of saving many human lives. A great impetus was given by these discoveries to the establishment of hygienic and other laboratories where the new science of bac-teriology was actively cultivated. Medicine, both as a science and an art, had entered upon a new era, already rich in achievement and still richer in promise of future good.

While Dr. Reed took the regular courses in pathol-ogy given in the laboratory and was interested in the subject, his special object was bacteriology, which is included in the Department of Pathology. In the con-duct of these courses there were associated with me at that time, Drs. Councilman, Abbott, Nuttall, and Flexner; and among others then engaged in research work in the laboratory I call to mind, Drs. Halsted, Lafleur, H. M. Thomas, Berkeley, W. T. Howard, Jr., Barker, Robb, Ghriskey, Randolph, Clement, Blackstein, Gilchrist, and Thayer.

Dr. Reed soon made a place for himself in this in-timate group of active workers. We early recognised that he possessed unusual aptitude for the work which he had undertaken, and that he combined with excel-lent endowment of mind a sincere, manly, and winning personality. The friendships formed with his teachers and co-workers at this period were strong and enduring.

Dr. Reed applied himself with great energy to his work in the laboratory, devoting to it daily a large part of his time and carrying it much beyond the regular class exercises. After he had acquired familiarity with technical methods, he undertook advanced and independent work. He attended post-mortem examinations and sometimes conducted them; moreover, he was accustomed to study for himself pathological material and cultures which he had obtained from autopsies. He followed and profited by the various investigations which were at that time in progress in the laboratory and the Hospital, and he was a regular attendant at the Hospital Medical Societies. Drs. Abbott, Flexner, and I were at that time engaged in the study of diphtheria, the toxin of which had been discovered two years previously, and the antitoxin of which was discovered by Behring in 1890. The investigations of hog-cholera made at this time by Dr. Clement and myself enabled Dr. Reed to become familiar with the hog-cholera bacillus, so that he had no difficulty later in recognising the resemblance to this bacillus of the micro-organism erroneously claimed by Sanarelli to be the cause of yellow fever. He also followed with great interest the studies of Drs. Councilman and Lafleur on amœbic dysentery, as well as investigations in the Hospital on the malarial parasite.

During the latter part of his stay in Baltimore Dr. Reed was assigned, at his own request, a special subject for research. This was the microscopical and experimental study of the so-called lymphoid nodules which are found in the liver in cases of typhoid fever. He succeeded in producing these nodules experimentally and demonstrated that they originated as small foci of dead liver cells. His paper upon this subject, published in the Reports of the Johns Hopkins Hospital, is a valuable contribution, and it embodies the results of his first original scientific investigation.[1]

When Dr. Reed left Baltimore in October, 1891, he was well trained in pathological and bacteriological methods, he had acquired a considerable amount of experience, and he was thoroughly fitted to make the best use of such opportunities as might present themselves to add to this experience and training, as well as to undertake original investigation. This was apparent to us at the time and was fully demonstrated by his subsequent career.

In 1893, when Dr. Reed was assigned to duty as curator of the Army Medical Museum and professor of bacteriology and clinical microscopy in the Army Medical School, he at once re-established relations with the Pathological Laboratory in Baltimore. He was a frequent visitor, together with his associate, Dr. Carroll, at the laboratory, and he kept in touch with the men and the work there. He often came to the Hospital Medical Society, at which he occasionally made contributions. I was often consulted by him regarding his own investigations, and his relations were likewise very intimate and cordial with Drs. Flexner, Abbott, and Thayer. He talked over with me the plan of the yellow fever work to be undertaken by the commission of which he was the head, and he kept me informed by letter and by conversation of the results of this work while it was in progress.

[1] Johns Hopkins Hosp. Rep., 1895, vol. 5, p. 379.

It is one of the greatest satisfactions and pleasures of my life to have enjoyed the relations of teacher and of friend with a man who has left a memory so respected and beloved, and who has conferred such inestimable benefits upon his country and upon mankind as Dr. Reed.

In October, 1891, Reed was sent to Dakota, and remained there until 1893, when he was ordered to duty in the office of the Surgeon-General in Washington. There he was made curator of the Army Medical Museum and professor of bacteriology and clinical microscopy in the United States Army Medical School, then just organised, and was at the same time promoted to be full surgeon with the rank of major. With this promotion his garrison life ended, after lasting eighteen years and including fifteen changes of station. Its influence on his own life and character is best described in the words of friends who speak from personal knowledge of him and of his environment during this period.

Dr. McCaw, in his excellent memoir of Dr. Reed, writes on the subject thus:

For a man like Reed, already an earnest student, no better preparation for his future could perhaps have been made. His early army service must have singularly tended to develop in him the very qualities most necessary to his final success. To the end of his life it was noticeable that, even when he had long given up

the practice of medicine for the work of the laboratory, he was, nevertheless, unexcelled at the bedside
for unerring diagnosis and sound judgment in treatment. So also were the experiments which robbed
yellow fever of its terrors especially remarkable for
simplicity, accuracy, and completeness, or they would
never have so quickly convinced the world of their
truth. Too much reverence for accepted teaching and
too little experience in grappling with difficulties unas-
sisted, and they might never have been conceived.

Major J. R. Kean spoke to the same effect as
follows at the memorial services held in memory
of Dr. Reed at Washington, in December, 1902:

In speaking of Dr. Reed as a medical officer we
should consider especially that part of his career with
which the members are least familiar, namely, from
his entrance into the army, in 1875, to his assignment
to duty in Washington, in 1893. With the latter date
began his career as a scientific man, although much of
his time during the last decade was given to examining
boards and other work of a military rather than a
scientific character, and the race horse spent much time
at the plough. These eighteen years of garrison duty
were, we may be sure, not wasted, yet the official
records tell us but little of them. . . . The work of
young army surgeons claims little space in the gazettes
or in the reports of military commanders, and in the
seventies and eighties the life was certainly not stimu-
lating to intellectual effort.
The surgeon shared with his comrades of the line

the tedium of marches and the monotonous sameness of Arizona summers and Dakota winters. And those with whom *bonne camaraderie* outweighed studious industry shared alike the afternoons of bottle-pool and beer, and the nightly seductions of draw-poker. But for medical officers it was redeemed by the study of our profession, which was then beginning to broaden out from ancient channels into the full flood of recent progress, and it was saved from triviality by those stern responsibilities of life and death which practice brings to all physicians. To lesser minds the limitations of such a life must have been narrowing, but for the eager industry and professional devotion of a Reed they made the roots strike deep; and when we are surprised at the rapid growth and splendid fruit of his career as a scientist, we must remember that in the post-surgeon's unmarked life the seed was germinated and the roots firmly set. But for the opportunities given him by his position in the army, however distinguished he might have become in other ways, it is safe to say that the work with which his fame will always be inseparably connected would never have been accomplished by him. During that long apprenticeship he acquired, too, that perfect familiarity with the conditions and limitations of army life which, combined with his scientific knowledge and sound judgment, made him the best sanitary inspector in the army and the court of last resort on all sanitary questions.

Dr. Reed's paper on " The Contagiousness of Erysipelas" was published in 1892, and from this time forward he was a constant contributor to medical periodicals, where his literary work shows the same excellence as everything else to which he put his hand. A full list of his publications is given at the end of this volume. They stand as witness to the indomitable energy and perseverance of the man as well as to his unusual intellectual endowments, for it must be remembered, that not only were these papers written during a single decade, but that the scientific researches which they record were all executed during the same space of time.

The discovery of the Klebs-Loeffler bacillus was a matter of extreme interest to Dr. Reed, and he used every means in his power to advance the practical benefits attendant on its demonstration. Early in 1894 he was invited by the Medical Society of the District of Columbia to open the discussion on a paper by Dr. Kinyoun, entitled, " The Prevention and Control of Diphtheria "; he conducted the debate with great earnestness and admirable command of the subject. He firmly believed that the Klebs-Loeffler bacillus was the cause of primary diphtheria, and that the disease was a local one, tending to become constitutional by the production of virulent toxins. A year later, January, 1895, in discussing diphtheria and its treatment by antitoxin, he said that he believed the production of antitoxin should be under municipal control and the serum tested by disinterested persons, so as to avoid imposition by unscrupulous men, actuated by the love of gain. On December 4, 1895, he struck the deathblow to the local opponents of antitoxin in a discussion on "The Clinical Aspects of Diphtheria" before the Medical Society in Washington. The president, Dr. S. S. Adams, thus describes the occasion:

A clinician of wide experience and recognised ability, while disclaiming any unfriendliness towards its use, had taken a decided stand against this serum, basing his remarks upon the statistics and arguments of a distinguished English laryngologist and a well-known American pediatrist. It seemed as if the pendulum were swinging toward the opposition when Walter Reed entered the forum—majestic, fearless, determined to conquer. With keen eyes fixed on his principal antagonist, he hurled his weapon of defence in unmistakable language, when he said: "You are theorising, while we are dealing with facts. If another friend of antitoxin arises and deals it such blows as Doctor —— has given it, the antitoxin-serum will be slaughtered in the house of its friends." In concluding his remarks came this appeal: "I myself almost feel like saying, with the reader of the paper, that the failure to use it in a case of human diphtheria is criminal; and I beg of you, that if you have not yet done so, when next you stand by the bedside of your patient afflicted with this disease, you do not, through any fear of its peculiar action, withhold this invaluable remedy."

In 1898, when the Spanish-American War broke out, Dr. Reed became extremely anxious to hold some responsible position in charge of sick soldiers. He knew that his experience peculiarly fitted him to do this work, since he was familiar with practical matters, such as the condition of the army, the routine of getting supplies, the manner of preserving the health of the soldiers, and all questions of general management, which were unknown to the civilian physicians and political doctors appointed to hold responsible positions over him. He made a strong effort to secure some such appointment, for which years of army work had so admirably fitted him, only to be chagrined and distressed when men with political influence were preferred, while he and other army surgeons were relegated to other unimportant positions. The records of our camps during the Spanish-American War afford, indeed, a valuable object lesson on the evils of allowing matters in which human safety depends upon technical knowledge and specialised training to be governed by political interest. For, not only is human life, under such conditions, at the mercy of ignorance, indifference, and greed, but the very men whose hands are tied by political usurpation of authority which should be theirs, are liable to undeserved blame for the evils they have striven to prevent, and our credit as a nation suffers in consequence.

No one felt this injustice more keenly than Dr. Reed; and in a conversation with a friend soon after the war was over, he spoke with extreme sadness of the fact that by such mismanagement on the part of the Secretary of War and others who should know better, the Army Medical Corps had been subjected to censure which it did not deserve. To use his own words, " The Army Medical Corps has received a black eye because of the neglect and incompetence of men who did not really belong to it."

The knowledge gained by our experience in Cuba and in our own Southern States shows only too plainly that there is but one remedy for such a state of things, and that a radical one, namely, the entire reorganisation of the Army Medical Corps with the object of investing it with authority necessary to carry out the measures and regulations which it enacts. So long as the Army Medical Corps is subject, in hygienic and sanitary matters, to the will of ignorant, inefficient, or unprincipled military officials, no improvement can be expected. During our recent war the army surgeon could recommend proper sanitary regulations, but he had no authority to enforce his recommendations. The value of camp cleanliness, pure water, and adequate sanitary arrangements might be appreciated by the medical authorities, but so long as the military officials refused to co-operate they were powerless to enforce the necessary regulations. If the military commander issued orders to enforce sanitary regulations they were carried out; but if not, they never went into effect, no matter how great the need for them might be. The mortality and suffering which resulted from this state of things would, it might be thought, have resulted in some measures for improvement, but no steps towards it have as yet been taken. Nothing, indeed, but a complete reorganisation of all matters connected with the medical department of the United States Army can produce any lasting benefit; and until this is done we are at the mercy, should war again be our fate, of the same ravages from disease which have already cost us so dear.

When, owing to the ignorance of untrained officials and the lack of organisation and method, typhoid fever broke out among the volunteer troops, Dr. Reed was made chairman of a committee to study its causation and modes of propagation. The other members were, Dr. V. C. Vaughan of the University of Michigan and Dr. E. O. Shakespeare of Philadelphia. The investigation, which covered more than a year, was remarkable for the patience and skill with which a vast number of details were collected and studied, and it marks a great advance in our knowledge of the disease. The report of the committee, under the title "Report of the Origin and Spread of Typhoid Fever in the United States Military Camps during the Spanish-American War of 1898," has only recently been issued by Government, for its publication required not only a considerable amount of time and work in order that so vast an amount of data might be available to the profession at large, but also demanded a liberal expenditure of money. The labor required has been supplied by the sole surviving member of the board, Dr. Vaughan, and the appropriation by Congress of the necessary funds is due, in large measure, to the interest and appreciation of the former Secretary of War, Mr. Elihu Root.

The report is issued in two large volumes, the first of which contains the reports on typhoid fever in all the different army divisions, with plots of distribution of regiments, regimental lists, temperature charts, and the conclusions reached after a careful study of the results; the second volume contains maps of the country over which typhoid fever was distributed. The book is a monumental work, which will always be of value as a basis of future study in the epidemiology of typhoid fever.

The most original and interesting point in the investigation is the proof that the infection of typhoid fever is spread in camps by the common fly and by contact with patients and infected articles, such as clothing, tentage, and utensils of all kinds, as well as by contaminated drinking water. Space forbids me to quote from it at length, but I give one or two extracts from the general statements and conclusions at its close.

Section 27—*Infected water was not an important factor in the spread of typhoid fever in the national encampments in* 1898.

There were probably local water supplies that became specifically infected with the typhoid fever bacillus, but infected water was not the great factor in the causation of this disease. It is possible that the piped water at Chickamauga became specifically contaminated. . . . However, that even at Chickamauga infected water was not the chief factor in the spread of typhoid fever is shown by the fact that regiments which did not drink piped water also became widely infected with the disease, and it is furthermore demonstrated by the fact that the spread of typhoid fever continued after the regiments had been moved to Knoxville, Tenn., and Lexington, Ky., at both which places the water supply was above suspicion.

Section 28—*Flies undoubtedly acted as carriers of the infection.*

Flies swarmed over the infected fecal matter in the pits, and then visited and fed upon the food prepared for the soldiers at the mess tents. In some instances where lime had been sprinkled over the contents of the pits flies with their feet whitened with lime were seen walking over the food. It is possible for the fly to carry the typhoid infection in two ways. In the first place, the fecal matter containing the germ may adhere to the fly and be mechanically transported. In the second place, it is possible that the typhoid bacillus may be deposited with its excrement. Since the above was written Hamilton has demonstrated that the house fly may, and does at times, transport the typhoid bacillus. . . . Fischer (Arch. f. Hygiene, Bd. 46, s. 274) has attempted to determine the duration of life of the typhoid bacillus in the bodies of flies fed on infected material, and places it at twenty-three days.

Section 29—*It is more than likely that men transported infected material on their persons, or in their clothing, and thus disseminated the disease.*

We have condemned the method which was followed in many of the camps, of detailing men from the ranks to act as orderlies at the hospitals. In some of the commands it was customary to detail 100 or more men from the line every morning. The most of these men were wholly ignorant of the nature of infection and the methods of disinfection. In fact, at one of the division hospitals we saw orderlies of this kind go from the hospital and partake of their midday meal without even washing their hands. These men handled not only the food they ate, but passed articles to their neighbours. It seems to us that a more certain method for the dissemination of an infectious disease could hardly have been invented.

Section 30—*Typhoid fever, as it developed in the regimental organisation, was characterised by a series*

*of company epidemics, each one having more or less
perfectly its own individual characteristics.*

The truth of this statement will be evident after the
inspection of the charts showing the distribution of
typhoid fever among the companies of the different
regiments. . . . Certain tents were badly infected
and the majority of all their inmates developed the
disease, while other tents wholly escaped. Blankets
and tentage became soiled with typhoid discharges,
and in this way the disease was propagated and carried
by the company wherever it went. We believe, therefore, that personal contact was a very important factor,
probably the most important, in the spread of the disease. That the floors, furniture, and bedding of barracks may become infected with typhoid fever, and
may continue to endanger the life and health of the
occupants for a long time is abundantly shown in the
records of military surgeons. . . . Our investigations certainly demonstrate that typhoid fever is not
only an infectious, but also a contagious disease; that
it may be transmitted from one person to another by
contact, and that the clothing, bedding, and rooms of
typhoid patients should be disinfected with as much
care as is now given to these matters in cases of diphtheria and scarlet fever.

Section 31—*It is probable that the infection was
disseminated to some extent through the air in the form
of dust.*

. . . The shell roads through the encampments at
Jacksonville were ground by the heavy army waggons
into an impalpable dust several inches thick. Along
these roads scavengers carted in half barrels fecal
matter containing the typhoid bacillus. The contents of

these tubs splashed and fell in the dust. On each side of these roads soldiers were encamped, and many dining tables were in close proximity to the roads. Local whirlwinds sometimes caught up large quantities of this dust and carried it considerable distances. After seeing these things we feel that we cannot exclude dust as a probable carrier of infection, notwithstanding the fact that it would probably be a very difficult thing to demonstrate scientifically that the disease was disseminated in this way.

In 1899, when the work of the Typhoid Commission was completed, Dr. Reed returned to Washington. Shortly afterward he was called upon to undertake investigations which really represent the first stage of his work in yellow fever, but before we take up the consideration of this, the central event of his life, let us pause for a moment to review the history of yellow fever in the past, in order that we may form a just conception of the condition of knowledge regarding it at the time the Yellow Fever Commission began its work.

CHAPTER IV

HISTORY OF YELLOW FEVER IN THE PAST

" Miserandaque venit
. . . lues, et lethifer annus,
Linquebant dulces animas, aut aegra trahebant corpora."
—Virgil, *Æneid,* Book III.

YELLOW FEVER was described by Osler in
1892 as " an acute febrile disorder of tropical or
subtropical climates, characterised by jaundice
and hemorrhages, and due to the action of a specific virus, the nature of which is not yet known." [1]
The course of the disease, according to the same
authority, is distinguished by a sudden onset without previous symptoms. There is frequently an
initial chill, associated with headache and pain in
the back and limbs, nausea and vomiting, constipa-
tion, and diminished urinary secretion. This first,
or *febrile,* stage lasts from a few hours to a few
days, and may or may not be accompanied by the
jaundice which gives the disease its name. It is followed by a remission, sometimes known as the *stage
of calm,* during which the temperature falls, and
the severity of the symptoms subsides. In favourable cases the disease now decreases and convales-

[1] " Practice of Medicine," 1892, p. 125.

cence sets in. In other instances, the third stage, known as *febrile reaction,* begins. The temperature again rises, all the symptoms become aggravated, the jaundice develops rapidly, and in many cases the symptom called " black vomit " takes place; this is the ejection of blood and gastric mucus altered by the acid juices of the stomach. Black vomit is usually regarded as a symptom belonging distinctively to yellow fever, but such is not the case, since material identical with it is brought up under other febrile conditions in which vomiting of blood occurs. It is not, therefore, necessarily a fatal symptom in yellow fever, though it is present only in the severer forms of the disease. Bleeding sometimes occurs from the gums and from the kidneys, while hæmorrhages into the skin are not uncommon. The mortality in yellow fever is very high, having ranged in different countries from 15 to 85 per cent. Convalescence is slow or rapid, according to the severity of the disease, and, in most cases, one attack insures against another.

In the treatment of yellow fever almost every known measure under the sun has been tried at different times, with indifferent success. Even inoculation with the poison of the rattlesnake was employed at Havana many years ago, and was asserted by some persons to have been of considerable value in certain forms of the disease. But this question, once of vital interest, has become of secondary importance now that the prevention or extinction of the disease has been shown to be possible. The forms of treatment which our present knowledge shows to be most profitable are given in Chapter XI, with other records of Dr. James Carroll's work.

Some of the older writers have objected to the name "yellow fever" (*fièvre jaune* in French and *fiebre amarilla* in Spanish) because the yellow tinge of the skin from which it is derived is present also in bilious fever. The name in common use among the Spaniards, "*el vomito negro*," is, perhaps, a better term.

At different periods in the earth's history both the old world and the new have been scourged by epidemics of yellow fever, which have never been arrested by any of the means employed for the purpose. On every occasion the disease has run its course unhindered, the only fact clearly determined being that its abatement was always preceded by cooler weather.

Some of the older writers claim that yellow fever was originally present in Africa, though Cortes found it in Mexico, where it was known as *matzlahuatt*. It was certainly unknown in Europe until after the discovery of America by Columbus.

The earliest authentic instance of it is an epidemic in Central America, in 1596, concerning which Mr. J. M. Keating, in his account of the epidemic in Memphis in 1878, speaks as follows:[2]

The first authentic record we have of the appearance of yellow fever is that which occurred in Central America, in 1596. Subsequently we hear of it in New England among the Indians, in 1618. After that in the Island of St. Lucia, in 1664, where it killed over 1411 out of a population of 1500 soldiers, a ratio of 1 in 1.06 of the whole number. We next hear of it in the same place, in 1665, when, out of 500 sailors, 200 died, being 1 in 2.5, and again in 1666, when every man, woman, and child of 5000 died. New York was visited by it for the first time in 1668; Boston in 1691 and again in 1693; Philadelphia was visited for the first time in 1695. In 1699 it again visited the latter city, the mortality being 220, which no doubt was very heavy, as the inhabitants were few in numbers, the town being only seventeen years old. Charleston, S. C., was also visited for the first time in 1699, but what the mortality was we have no means of knowing.

Between the years 1702 and 1800 yellow fever appeared in the United States, according to Keating, thirty-five times, in localities varying from Pensacola to Nantucket Island, but showing a

[2] "History of the Yellow Fever Epidemic of 1878," J. M. Keating, 1879.

marked preference for the cities of the South. Among these visitations was the epidemic in Philadelphia in 1793, when the death rate was 1 in 10 of the population. Between the years 1800 and 1879, when Keating's book was issued, yellow fever visited the United States *every year* with two exceptions, although it was epidemic on only a few occasions. The great epidemics during this period were that of New Orleans in 1853, in which there were 29,020 cases with 8101 deaths, a mortality of 27.91 per cent.; and that of Memphis in 1878, when there were 17,600 cases with 5150 deaths, a mortality of 1 in 3.3. In 1878 the disease also raged extensively throughout the Southern States in general, reaching as far north as Virginia.

Up to the time of the Philadelphia epidemic of 1793 yellow fever seems to have been accepted without question as the visitation of God, and no theories in regard to its origin or mode of transmission were developed. In 1793, however, when the interest of the medical profession in Philadelphia was focussed on the disease, two hypotheses as to the manner in which it originated were brought forward. One of them was that of direct importation, probably from the West Indies, and this was supported by the College of Physicians. The other view, held by some of the best authorities in the city, and in particular by Dr. Benjamin

Rush, was that of a local origin, that is to say, of spontaneous generation under appropriate conditions of filth, heat, and moisture.

The manner by which the disease was propagated also became the subject of discussion, although definite theories in regard to this point were slow to develop. In 1793 the large majority of physicians held that yellow fever was transmitted through direct contact with the infected individual, although there were a few who believed its extension was due to the diffusion, through the agency of the air, of morbid exhalations, themselves the offspring of organic decomposition. The latter doctrine gradually gained ground, until, at last, the physicians of Philadelphia became divided into two hostile parties, and, says La Roche, from whom I quote, " From this moment may be dated the origin of the interminable dispute about contagion and non-contagion which has continued ever since to occupy the attention of the medical profession in this and in other countries."[3]

Priority in the publication of views on the non-contagion theory was for many years the subject of much discussion. La Roche tells us that Dr. Nathaniel Potter, of Baltimore (died 1843), in an essay on contagion published some time after the Philadelphia epidemic, claims that in October,

[3] " Yellow Fever," by R. La Roche, M. D., 1855.

1793, he had written to Dr. Rush emphasising the domestic origin and the non-contagious character of the epidemic diseases of the Eastern Shore of Maryland, and had then expressed the opinion that fevers arising from vegetable decomposition are non-contagious, suggesting at the same time that the yellow fever epidemic raging in Philadelphia was also, as he expresses it, "devoid of that property." Dr. Potter further states that in the summer of 1795, believing that he was at that time the only person in America who denied the contagious character of the disease, and that his opinion could be sustained by facts, he proposed to embody his views in a thesis, but was dissuaded from doing so by Dr. Wistar. This claim to priority is explicit, but it is sustained only by a letter, not made public until 1818, and however true it is that Dr. Potter entertained such views, his claim to priority must yield to that of others who were less tardy in making their opinions public. Other claimants to the distinction of first formulating the doctrine of non-contagion are Dr. Davidge of Baltimore, in the Baltimore Federal Gazette of November 30, 1797, and Dr. Charles MacLean, an English authority, who unhesitatingly ascribes the belief in non-contagion, which appeared in Philadelphia about 1798, to the influence of a dissertation by himself on the source of epidemic diseases, originally

issued in Calcutta, in 1796, and reprinted in Philadelphia in 1797.

According to La Roche, however, there can be
no doubt that to Dr. Jean Deveze of Philadelphia
belongs the distinction of first publicly enunciat-
ing the non-contagion theory. Dr. Deveze arrived
in Philadelphia from the West Indies at the beginning of the epidemic of 1793, and was soon
after placed at the head of a hospital opened at
Bush Hill, where he had ample means of observing the disease. In 1794, a year before Dr. Potter
proposed writing his thesis, Dr. Deveze published
a description of the epidemic of 1793, and in this
essay, which has never, in the opinion of La Roche,
received the attention it deserves, he boldly pro-
claims the non-contagious character of the disease,
assigning facts analogous to those advanced by
subsequent writers and adducing arguments similar to theirs.[4]

As the facts brought out by the epidemic of 1793
in Philadelphia were gradually disseminated, a
change became perceptible in the opinion of the
leading physicians there and elsewhere as to the
question of contagion. Dr. Rush, who in 1793 was

[4] "An Inquiry into and Observations upon the Causes and
Effects of the Epidemic which Raged in Philadelphia from the
Month of August till toward the Middle of December, 1793."
By Jean Deveze, Philadelphia, 1794.

himself a decided supporter of the contagion theory, modified his views in the partial epidemic
of 1794, and some years later published a formal
recantation of what he had come to consider an
error, stating that although he was aware of the
influence which changes in medical opinion have
upon a physician's reputation, he " should consider
as small the total sacrifice of his own, could it avert
the evils which are connected with a belief in the
importation of pestilential diseases, and insure to
the world the benefits which would necessarily
flow from the establishment of the doctrines of
non-contagion." In a subsequent part of his work
he even goes so far as to beg forgiveness from the
friends of science and humanity if the publication
of his opinion in favour of the contagion theory
had exercised any influence in increasing the misery and mortality attendant upon the disease, adding that such was the pain he felt in recollecting
that he had entertained and propagated it, that " it
would long, and perhaps always, deprive him of
the pleasure he might otherwise have derived from
a review of his attempts to fulfil the public duties
of his situation."

Contagionists at this period were divided, according to La Roche, into three classes: first, those
who believed the disease to be invariably contagious, the power of communication being more

actively displayed in crowded, ill-ventilated, and
filthy places; second, those who believed the disease was naturally endowed with contagious properties, but that these required an impure atmosphere for their manifestation; third, those who
considered that the disease had not naturally any
contagious properties at all, but could acquire them
through the influence of favourable conditions,
such as filth and bad air or water. The third of
these opinions, namely, that the disease becomes
contagious only under unfavourable conditions,
was upheld by many of the best physicians, including Dr. Rush, up to the time of his recantation, and
all old writings on yellow fever contain constant
references to the effect of heat, moisture, and
organic decomposition on the spread of the disease.

The doctrine of local origin gained ground at
the same time as that of non-contagion; indeed,
there seems to have been a general impression that
direct importation implied contagion, while non-
contagion assumed a local origin.

As would naturally be expected, the occurrence
of each epidemic by which some region of the
country was swept stimulated men's minds to investigation of the problems involved in the disease,
and, accordingly, we find epochs in the development of knowledge regarding it associated with the
years marked by its most formidable outbreaks.

With the Philadelphia epidemic of 1793 the non-contagion theory, as we have seen, found entrance, and the years immediately following it were fruitful in contributions to the support of that view.

In 1819 a mild epidemic of yellow fever occurred in Baltimore, and we then find one of the citizens, consulted on the subject, writing to the mayor that:

> The very fact that individuals every way competent to judge of the matter are now found opposing the doctrine of contagion is in itself evidence of such high authority that nothing short of so overwhelming a truth could have removed their prejudices and changed their opinions. . . . Of the hundreds and thousands who declare and believe yellow fever to be a contagious disease very few have ever seen it; and those who have ventured to look upon it came to the sight with all the horrors which must be felt in the field of battle, expecting every moment a shaft of contagion to transfix their liver; of course they were badly qualified to make a cool, dispassionate inquiry, whilst our distinguished non-contagionists have had rational cause to triumph over all their terrors and think like men.[5]

The opinions which are quoted in this and other letters show that while the doctrine of contagion was still accepted by the uneducated and preju-

[5] Series of Letters and Other Documents Relating to the Late Epidemic of Yellow Fever. Baltimore, Second Dispensary, 1820.

diced, it was generally discredited among those carrying authority.

In 1853 occurred the great epidemic in New Orleans, and two years later, in 1855, La Roche published his monumental work on the history of yellow fever, which up to the present time has been the great authority on the subject and will always remain the most complete source of information as to it in the past. La Roche reviews all the ground covered by investigation from the time when the cause and propagation of yellow fever were first under discussion, and sums up the evidence in favor of local origin and non-contagion.

A few years later the pendulum had begun to incline to the other side. In 1867 some mild epidemics at New Orleans, Galveston, and Indianola induced the United States Government to send a commission to inquire into their cause and character. The official report of this commission states that the direct importation of the disease is, in its opinion, fully established, the source, in that particular instance, being Vera Cruz, Mexico, and Havana. The question of contagion is not discussed, being apparently accepted as a matter of course.

In 1878 occurred the great epidemic of Memphis, which belongs to the experience of the present generation; and in the next year an eye-witness,

Mr. J. M. Keating, published the vivid and interesting account of it already mentioned, which contains a discussion of all the knowledge acquired in regard to the disease up to that date. He gives a number of different theories which had been advanced during the years immediately preceding his work, some of which are very ingenious, not to say fantastic.

Dr. J. M. Clements, of Louisville, attributed the yellow fever poison to some order of fungus plants indigenous to the tropics, but as yet undiscovered. Dr. Ford, of St. Louis, believed in a principle of fermentation, by which yellow fever remained existent in the form of dry particles of dust everywhere that it had once prevailed; cold, however, repressed the activity of these germs, in so far as cold rendered persons less receptive and prevented their bodies from being in a condition to induce the fermentation of the dry dust. Professor P. Stillé, of Mobile, advanced a novel theory which attributed the disease to the influence of the Gulf Stream. Dr. Labadie favoured the "explosive theory," namely, the theory that the disease was caused by a peculiar subtle poison which exploded in the air like an inflammable substance, and that persons who inhaled or swallowed it, in greater or less quantity, fell under its influence after a certain time. Dr. Warren Stone, of New Orleans, in company with many others, upheld the wave, or cycle theory.

The best authorities, however, seem to have inclined to the opinion that the disease was due to a specific germ, a view expressed in a somewhat indefinite manner by the medical experts appointed by Congress in December, 1878, to investigate the disease. In their report they state that:

It (yellow fever) is a specific disease produced by the introduction into the human organism of a specific poison, and though this specific poison has never been chemically or microscopically demonstrated, nor in any way made evident to the human senses, we deem it safe to assume that it is material and particular, is endowed with ordinary properties, and is subject to the ordinary laws of material substance. We also hold that it is organic—is endowed with the vital properties of growth and reproduction; that it is not malarial, but the concurrence of local conditions favourable to the evolution of it seems to be necessary to the evolution of yellow fever epidemics.

It is about this time that *fomites,* a term which for the next twenty years did constant service, begins to come into prominence. Dr. L. S. Tracy, in a number of the Popular Science Monthly about 1878, says:

Yellow fever occupies a singular position between the contagious and non-contagious diseases. The poison is not like that of smallpox, directly communicable from a sick person to a well one; but, although the emanations of the sick are connected with the spread of the disease, they seem to require an appropriate nidus in which to germinate and develop. This nidus must be warm and moist, and there the germs, whatever they are, lie and grow, or in some way develop until they are able to migrate. The germs are portable and may be conveyed in baggage or merchandise (*fomites*) for hundreds or thousands of miles. If not so conveyed the spread of the disease is very slow. In 1822, in New York, when it gained a foothold in Rector Street, it appeared to travel about 40 feet a day until killed by the frost. It often leaves a house or a block intact, going round it and attacking those beyond with no assignable reason. A thin board partition seems to have stopped it on Governor's Island, in 1856, and an instance is related where it attacked the sailors in all the berths of one side of a ship before crossing to the other. Such apparent vagaries, in the present state of our knowledge, are inexplicable.

From all these data it would appear that knowledge of yellow fever had at this period advanced very little beyond its status in 1793, if, indeed, it had not in some respects receded; for, although the contagion theory in its original sense was abandoned, that is to say, the direct transmission of the disease from one person to another, after the fashion of smallpox and other eruptive fevers, was no longer accepted, the theory of its conveyance by means of fomites was now fully established.

For twenty years after this, knowledge of yellow fever remained stationary, and, in 1898, the officers of the United States Marine Hospital Service issued a report in which they sum up the status of knowledge at that period as follows:

While yellow-fever is a communicable disease, it is not contagious in the ordinary acceptation of the term, but is spread by the infection of places and articles of bedding, clothing, and furniture. This is a process requiring several days (extrinsic infection), and during this period the yellow fever patient is as harmless as one suffering from a surgical complaint. . . . More recently the idea has been advanced that probably the germ of yellow fever enters the general circulation through the respiratory organs in some obscure manner, and incubating in the blood directly poisons this life-giving stream. However this may be, the present opinion is that one has not to contend with an organism or germ which may be taken into the body with food or drink, but with an almost inexplicable poison so insidious in its approach and entrance that no trace is left behind.

This is practically the last official statement under the old order and the last defence of the old-fashioned theories on yellow fever.

CHAPTER V.

INSECTS AND DISEASE

> " Imo muscas tum infirmorum tum cadaverum succo saturatas, mox in alias domos vicinas transmigrantes dum sordibus suis comestibilia inficiunt hominibus iis vescentibus contagium attulisse Mercurialis refert."—ATHANASIUS KIRCHER, *Scrutinium Physico-Medicum, etc.*, 1659, p. 247.

EXPERIMENTAL evidence proving that insects play an important part in the transmission of disease is of recent date, but suggestions to that effect are found scattered through literature for a number of years. Indeed, the early history of almost every infectious or contagious disease contains some reference to its supposed transmission by means of flies or other insects. Anthrax, cholera, typhoid fever, malaria, tuberculosis, leprosy, the plague, yellow fever, and many other less well-known diseases have been associated by early writers with insects as a mode of transmission. Anyone interested in the subject will find it exhaustively treated in Nuttall's monograph in the Johns Hopkins Hospital Reports for 1899.[1]

[1] " On the rôle of insects, arachnids, and myriapods, as carriers in the spread of bacterial and parasitic diseases of man and

The earliest of all allusions, so far as I can discover, is found in a treatise called *"De Regimine Pestilentico,"* which appeared in 1498, and is attributed to Bishop Knud of Aarhus, Denmark. Athanasius Kircher, a learned priest and naturalist of the seventeenth century, went farther, perhaps, than anyone towards a clear understanding of the part played by insects as carriers of disease. In his interesting work, *"Scrutinium Physico-Medicum,"* etc., published at Rome in 1659, he says: "Flies carry the plague," and again, "There can be no doubt that flies feed on the internal secretions of the diseased and dying, then flying away, they deposit their excretions on the food in neighbouring dwellings, and persons who eat it are thus infected."

Ambroise Paré, in his description of the battle-field of St. Quentin in 1557, strikes the same note when he says: [2] "We saw more than half a league round us the earth all covered with the dead; and hardly stopped there, because of the stench of the dead men and their horses; and so many blue and green flies rose up from them, bred of the moisture of their bodies and the heat of the sun, that when

animals." A critical and historical study, by G. H. F. Nuttall, M. D., Ph. D., Johns Hopkins Hosp. Rep., 1899, vol. VIII., p. 1.

[2] "Ambroise Paré and his Times," by Stephen Paget, 1897.

they were up in the air they hid the sun. It was wonderful to hear them buzzing; and where they settled, there they infected the air, and brought the plague with them "; and he adds, quaintly: " *Mon petit maistre,* I wish you had been with me, to experience the smells and make report thereof to them that were not there."

The first person to establish the fact that insects act as carriers of disease on a scientific basis was Dr., now Sir, Patrick Manson, in 1880. He demonstrated that the mosquito acts as the intermediary host of the Filaria Sanguinis Hominis, and is thus directly instrumental in the production of chyluria, elephantiasis, lymph-scrotum, etc. Manson's description of the part played by the mosquito under these circumstances is as follows: [3]

Should a certain species of mosquito which has fed on the blood of a filaria-infested individual be examined immediately after feeding, the blood contained in the stomach of the insect will be found to contain large numbers of living filariæ. If a second mosquito be examined three or four hours after it has similarly fed, it will be found that the blood corpuscles in its distended abdomen have, in great measure, parted with the hæmoglobin and that the blood plasma has become thickened, though not coagulated. If attention be directed to the filariæ in the thickened blood, it will

[3] " Tropical Diseases. A Manual of the Diseases of Warm Climates," 1898.

be seen that many of them are actively engaged in endeavouring to escape from their sheaths. The diffused hæmoglobin has so thickened the blood plasma that it has become viscid and holds, as it were, the sheath. This viscosity of the blood seems to prompt the filariæ to endeavour to escape from their sheaths. They become restless and excited, alternately retiring toward the tail, and then rushing forward against the head end of the sheath in frantic efforts to escape. After a time the majority succeed in effecting a breach, and in wriggling themselves free from the sheaths which had hitherto enclosed them. The filariæ now swim free in the blood and the character of their movements once more undergoes a remarkable change. Hitherto, though active enough in wriggling about, the parasite did not materially change its position on the slide, but now, having become free, it moves about from place to place—locomotes—in fact. If we dissect a mosquito at a somewhat later period after feeding, it will be found that the stomach of the insect, though still full of blood, contains very few filariæ, although their empty sheaths can be seen in abundance. If, however, we break up with needles the thorax of the insect and tease out the muscular tissue, we shall find that the filariæ after discarding their sheaths have quitted the stomach and entered the thoracic muscles óf the insect, among which they can now be seen, moving languidly. By a course of serial dissections of filariated mosquitoes, we can ascertain that in the thorax of the insect the parasite enters upon a metamorphosis which takes from six to seven days to complete—a metamorphosis eventuating in the formation of a mouth, of an alimentary canal, and of a peculiar trilobed tail, as well as in an enormous increase in the size and activity of the young parasite.

About a week after the time of feeding, the mosquito, in the ordinary course of nature, lays her eggs on the surface of stagnant water, and thereafter dies, falling into the water. It is conjectured that the filaria, now a formidable-looking and a very active animal, about one-sixteenth of an inch in length, escapes from the dead body of the insect, and thus, in drinking water, it obtains a chance of gaining access to the stomach of a human host. It is believed that it bores its way through the wall of the stomach, through the intervening tissues, and finally enters the lymphatic trunks. Arrived in one of these, it attains sexual maturity, fecundation is effected, and in due course of time new generations of embryo filariæ are poured into the lymph. These, passing through the glands—if such intervene—by way of the thoracic duct and left sub-clavian vein, or by the lymphatics of the upper part of the body, appear in the circulation. Such is the life-history of *filaria nocturna;* man is its definitive host, the mosquito its intermediate host. It is manifest that filarial periodicity is an adaptation of the habits of the mosquito parasite to that of the mosquito.

These conclusions of Manson's were subsequently confirmed by the experiments of Dr. Bancroft, in Australia, and of Dr. J. R. Lewis, in India, as well as those of Dr. Sonsino, in Egypt.

In 1883 an admirable paper by Dr. A. F. A. King on "Insects and Disease—Mosquitoes and Malaria," appeared in the Popular Science

Monthly for September of that year. The object
of this paper, it is stated, is " to present a series of
facts with regard to the so-called malarial poison,
and to show how they may be explicable by the
supposition that the mosquito is the real source of
diseases, rather than the inhalation or cutaneous ab-
sorption of a marsh vapour." The facts presented
by Dr. King are evidently the result of close observation and able reasoning, and they show an extensive acquaintance with the literature of the subject.
He had no experimental evidence to adduce in
support of his theory, but he handles his hypotheti-
cal material in a masterly manner, and offers a
stable foundation for further investigation. He
shows that the distribution, spread, and general
characteristics of malaria all correspond with the
life-history of the mosquito; also that mosquitoes
are common wherever malaria is prevalent; and
the conclusions he draws as to the possibility of
protection from malaria by destruction of mosquitoes are just what subsequent experiments have
demonstrated to be true. His own words are:
" While the data to be presented cannot be held
to prove the theory, they may go so far as to initiate
and encourage experiments and observations by
which the truth or fallacy of the views now held
may be demonstrated."

Further suggestions on the subject were made by

several observers, the most important of them being Koch, in 1884, and Laveran (independently), in the same year. It is, however, first to Dr. Manson and then to Major Ronald Ross of the British Army that we are indebted for a clear and definite knowledge of the part played by mosquitoes in the transmission of malaria.

The fact that the red blood corpuscles of vertebrates may contain within them certain parasites had been known for some time. These parasites are divided into three groups, one of which is found in reptiles, another in oxen (being the cause of Texas fever), and a third, which has received the name of *hæmamæbidæ*, in man. This third group includes the parasite of malarial fever, which exists under three varieties, corresponding to the three forms of the disease, tertian, quartan, and remittent. All the species have a close resemblance to each other and all contain the typical melanin of malarial fever. The youngest parasites are found as minute *amæbulæ*, living within the red blood corpuscle, and generally containing granules of this melanin derived from the hæmoglobin of the corpuscle. When these *amæbulæ* reach maturity they reproduce themselves in the ordinary asexual manner by means of spores, but they also, at one time in their life-history, undergo sexual reproduction through the formation of *gameto-*

cytes, and it is in the life-history of these *gameto-cytes* that the solution of the malarial problem lies. Long before Manson's time they were observed to circulate in the blood of their hosts without, apparently, performing any function whatever. As soon, however, as they are withdrawn from the circulation they are seen to swell up and liberate themselves from the enclosing capsule, after which some of them emit a number of long motile filaments. These filaments can then be seen to struggle wildly and sometimes to break from the parent cell, darting away among the corpuscles and leaving the residue of the *gametocyte,* with its melanin, an inert mass. A hot controversy concerning the nature of this phenomenon had been in existence ever since it was discovered. Laveran, who first observed it, considered that the motile filaments are living organs and constitute a stage in the life-history of the parasite. Bignami, and others of the Italian school, held to the old theory that it is a retrogressive phenomenon, a distinct disintegration of the parasite due to its death *in vitro.* At this point the controversy rested for a time, except that Laveran and his followers thought that the motile filaments were meant to lead a saprophytic existence, but they did not offer any explanation as to how they could escape from the body in order to do so.

Manson accepted the view that the *gametocytes* are living organisms, and he considered that the fact of their appearance only after the abstraction of the blood must have some definite purpose in the life scheme of the parasite. What this purpose was he set himself to discover.

He had already pushed the method of inductive reasoning to a brilliantly successful issue in his discovery of the development of the *filaria nocturna* within the body of the mosquito, and he pursued the same plan here. It is, of course, evident that the malarial parasite, like all others, must pass from host to host, since all known parasites are capable not only of entering the host, but of leaving him, either themselves or by their progeny. Here, in Manson's opinion, lay the explanation of the fact that the motile filaments appear only after abstraction of the blood. The phenomenon, though usually observed in a preparation for the microscope, is really meant to occur within the stomach cavity of some suctorial insect, and constitutes the first step in the life-history of the parasite outside the vertebrate host. Supposing this to be the case, the connection between malarial fever and low-lying areas in warm countries suggested that the suctorial insect must be the mosquito. This view proved to be correct, although Manson's first idea that the motile filaments are spores which escape from the *gametocytes* in the stomach cavity of the mosquito and then occupy and infest the tissues of the insect was afterwards disproved by the experiments of W. G. MacCallum.

MacCallum showed that the motile filaments were not spores, but *microgametes, i. e.,* bodies of the nature of spermatozoa. As soon as the *gametocytes,* which are sexual cells, male and female, are ingested by a suctorial insect they begin their proper functions: the male *gametocyte* emits a variable number of *microgametes* (the motile filaments), which wander to and fro in search of the female *gametocytes.* The female contains a single *macrogamete,* or ovum, which is fertilised by one of the *microgametes,* and becomes a *zygote.* As soon as this discovery of MacCallum's was announced, Manson saw the importance of its bearing on the mosquito theory, for if the motile filaments did not infect the insect, it was probably the function of the *zygote* to do so, and this view proved correct, although it was some time before it was established.

Towards the end of the year 1894 Manson communicated his theory concerning the mosquito to Major Ronald Ross, who at once set himself to investigate it in the malarial districts in India, where he was then stationed.

The task so lightly commenced [Ross says], was, as a matter of fact, one of so arduous a nature that we must attribute its accomplishment largely to good fortune. The method adopted—the only method which could be adopted—was to feed gnats[4] (mosquitoes) of various species on persons whose blood contained the *gametocytes,* and then to examine the insects carefully for the parasites which by hypothesis the *gametocytes* were expected to develop into. This required not only familiarity with the histology of gnats, but a laborious search throughout the whole tissues of each individual insect examined—a work of at least two or three hours for each individual, but the serial labour involved was the smallest part of the difficulty. Both the form and appearance of the object I was in search of, and the species of gnat in which I might expect to find it, were absolutely unknown quantities. We could make no attempt to predict the appearance which the parasite would assume in the gnat; while, owing to the general distribution of malarial fever in India, the species of insect engaged in the propagation of the disease could scarcely be determined by a comparison of the prevalence of different kinds of gnats at different spots with the prevalence of the fever at those spots. In short, I was obliged to rely simply on the careful examination of hundreds of gnats, first of one species and then of another, all fed on patients suffering from malarial fever—in the hope of one day finding the clue I was in search of. Needless to say that nothing but the most convincing theory, such as Manson's theory

---

[4] Major Ross uses the word " gnat " for mosquito throughout the article.

was, would have supported or justified so difficult an enterprise.[5]

For nearly two years and a half the search was almost entirely negative, and Major Ross had begun to despair, when fortune unexpectedly placed the clue in his hands. In a bottleful of larvæ, brought by a native from an unknown source, there were a number of newly hatched mosquitoes, belonging to a species with spotted wings and boat-shaped eggs, which Major Ross had only recently observed and of which he did not know the name. Eight of these mosquitoes were fed on a patient whose blood contained *" crescentic gametocytes "* and then examined; six of them were dissected prematurely, but the seventh when examined cell by cell gave the following results:

The tissues of the stomach (which was now empty owing to the meal of malarial blood taken by the insect four days previously being digested) were reserved to the last. On turning to this organ I was struck by observing, scattered on its outer surface, certain oval or round cells of about two to three times the diameter of a red blood corpuscle—cells which I had never before seen in any of the hundreds of mosquitoes examined by me. My surprise was complete when I next detected within each of these cells *a few granules of the characteristic coal-black melanin of malarial*

[5] " Malaria and Mosquitoes." *Nature*, 1900, vol. 61, p. 522.

fever—a substance quite unlike anything usually found in mosquitoes. Next day the last of the remaining spotted-winged insects was dissected. It contained precisely similar cells, each of which possessed the same melanin; only the cells in the second mosquito were *somewhat larger than those in the first.* . . . .

These fortunate observations solved the malarial problem. As a matter of fact the cells were the *zygotes of the parasite of remittent fever growing in the tissues of the gnat;* and the gnat with spotted wings and boat-shaped eggs in which I found them belonged (as I subsequently ascertained) to the genus *anopheles.* Of course it was impossible absolutely to prove at the time, on the strength of these two observations alone, that the cells found by me in the gnats were indeed derived from *hæmamœbidæ* sucked up by the insects in the blood of the patients on whom they had fed;—this proof was obtained by subsequent investigations of mine; but . . . the clue was obtained: it was necessary only to follow it up— an easy matter.

The further experiments by means of which Major Ross established beyond any possibility of doubt that the cells containing the melanin of malaria are really *zygotes* will be found in the interesting article upon which I have already made such liberal demands. I must confine myself to abstracting from it a brief account of the life-history of the *zygotes.*

After fertilisation of the *macrogamete* has taken

place in the stomach cavity of the gnat, the fertilised parasite, or *zygote,* has the power of working
its way through the mass of blood contained in the
stomach, of penetrating the wall of the organ, and
of affixing itself on, or just under, its *outer coat.*
Here it first appears about thirty-six hours after
the insect is fed, as a "pigmented cell," that is, a
little oval body about the size of a large red corpuscle, which contains the granules of melanin possessed by the parent *gametocyte* from which the
macrogamete originally came. In this position it
shows no sign of movement, but begins to grow rapidly, to acquire a thickened capsule, and to project
from the outer wall of the stomach to which it is
attached into the body cavity of the insect host. At
the end of six days, if the temperature of the body
be sufficiently high (about 80° F.), the diameter of
the *zygote* has increased to about eight times what
it was at first. If the stomach of an infected insect
be extracted at this stage it can be seen by a low
power of the microscope to be studded with a number of attached spheres, which have something the
appearance of warts on a finger. These are the
large *zygotes,* which have now reached maturity.
Every *zygote* now, as it increases in size, divides
into *meres,* each of which next becomes a *blastophore,* carrying a number of *blasts* attached to its
surface. Finally, the *blastophore* vanishes, leav-

ing the thick capsule of the *zygote* packed with thousands of *blasts*. The capsule then *ruptures* and allows the *blasts* to escape into the body fluids of the insect.

The question of importance which now arises is: How do the *blasts* which are the spores, and therefore the progeny of the *zygotes,* carry on the life-history of the parasite to a further stage? What is their function? It is evident that a knowledge of the mode of infection in malarial fever depends on the answer to this question. The *zygotes,* as has been said, become ripe and rupture, scattering the *blasts* into the body cavity of the insect. Then, by some process, apparently owing to the circulation of the fluids of the insect's body, the *blasts* find their way into every part of the mosquito.

Beyond this it was difficult to go, but at last, after examining the head and thorax of one insect, I found a large gland consisting of a central duct surrounded by large grape-like cells. My astonishment was great when I found that many of these cells were closely packed with the *blasts,* which are not in the least like any normal structure found in the mosquito. Now I did not, at this time, know what this gland is. It was speedily found, however, to be a large racemose gland consisting of six lobes, three lying in each side of the insect's neck. The ducts of the lobes finally unite in the common channel which runs along the under surface of the head and enters *the middle*

stylet, or lancet, of the insect's proboscis. It was impossible to avoid the obvious conclusion. Observation
after observation showed that the *blasts* collect within
the cells of this gland. It is the salivary or poison gland
of the insect, similar to the salivary gland found in
many insects, the function of which in the gnat had
already been discovered—although I was not aware of
the fact. *That function is to secrete the fluid which is
injected by the insect when it punctures the skin,*
fluid which causes the well-known irritation of the
puncture, and which is probably meant either to prevent the contraction of the torn capillaries or the
coagulation of the ingested blood. . . . The *blasts* must
evidently pass down the ducts of the salivary gland
into the wound made by the proboscis of the insect,
and thus cause *infection in a fresh vertebrate host.*

For the experiments by which Major Ross confirmed the truth of this observation I must again
refer the reader to the original article. Suffice it to
say that he was able to establish conclusively this
last link in the chain, and thus in his own words, to
" complete the original and fundamental observations on the life-history of the *hæmamœbidæ* in
mosquitoes."

In 1899 the expedition sent to Sierra Leone by
the Liverpool Tropical School of Medicine, of
which Major Ross was a member, confirmed the
results of his experiments in every respect, and his
work has also received support from other sources,
especially through the labours of Italian scientists.

The discovery of the connection between the mosquito (of the genus *Anopheles*) and malaria was received with great interest not only by the scientific world, but by the laity, and it has been put to a practical test in the protection of towns and districts from malaria through the systematic destruction of the mosquito.

While there is no doubt that the establishment of a connection between the mosquito and malaria led directly up to the discovery of the transmission of yellow fever by the same means, yet the first suggestion of a relation between the mosquito and yellow fever preceded the investigation of the origin of malaria by a good many years, and in order to follow it from its inception we must retrace our steps.

So far as I can find, the first person to suggest that insects play a part as carriers of yellow fever was Dr. J. C. Nott of Mobile, in 1848, in a paper entitled "On the Cause of Yellow Fever." Nott first disputes the then accepted doctrine that malaria was disseminated by means of a gaseous or molecular emanation from the earth's surface, dismissing it as wholly inadequate. He refers to the theory of transmission of disease through insects as no novelty, and mentions Kircher, as well as others who supported it in the past, after which he reviews a number of facts characteristic of malaria that are readily explicable on the hypothesis of insect transmission, but on no other.

Nott then describes the characteristics of yellow fever and shows that they, as well as many of the peculiarities noted in connection with it, such as its appearing on one side of the ship without infecting the other, are comprehensible, like those of malaria, only on the theory of insect transmission. "With these facts before us," he says, " how much more easily may we account for the spread of yellow fever from a focus, by the insect theory than by the malarial hypothesis." He also argues that the insect theory of yellow fever explains many of the facts which then presented difficulties to both contagionists and non-contagionists. " It is probable," he says, "that yellow fever is carried by an insect or animalcule bred on the ground, and in what manner it makes its impression on the system is but surmise—but unless the animalcule is, like that of psora, bred in the system, we could no more expect it to be contagious than the bite of a serpent. We may, therefore, easily understand that it can at the same time be transported in the form of a germ and yet not be contagious."

To Dr. Carlos J. Finlay of Havana, president of the Superior Board of Health of Cuba, belongs the credit of first formulating a definite theory as to the transmission of yellow fever by means of the mosquito, which he embodied in a paper read before the Royal Academy of Havana on August 11, 1881, under the title, "The Mosquito Hypothetically Considered as the Agent of Transmission of Yellow Fever."

Dr. Finlay's theory as stated in this paper is as follows:

Let us now consider by what means the mosquito might transmit the yellow fever, if that disease happens to be really transmissible through the inoculation of blood. The first and most natural idea would be that the transmission might be effected by the virulent blood which the mosquito has sucked, amounting to 5 to 7 cubic millimetres, and which, if the insect happens to die before completing its digestion, would be in excellent condition to retain during a long period its infecting properties. It might also be supposed that the same blood that the mosquito discharges as excrement, after having bitten a yellow fever patient, might be dissolved in drinking water, whereby the infection might be conveyed, if the latter were susceptible of penetrating by the mouth. But the experiments of Ffirth and other considerations arising from my personal ideas, regarding the pathogenesis of yellow fever, forbid my taking into account either of these modes of propagation. . . . A valuable collection of microphotographs from preparations made by our corresponding member, Surgeon-General Sternberg, showed what to me appeared to be a most striking feature, namely, that the red blood corpuscles are discharged unbroken in the hæmorrhages of yellow fever. This

DR. CARLOS J. FINLAY

who first promulgated the theory of the transmission of yellow fever
by the mosquito

fact, taken into consideration with the circumstance that these hæmorrhages are often unattended with any perceptible break in the blood vessels, while, on the other hand, they constitute a most essential clinical symptom of the disease, led me to infer that the principal lesion of yellow fever should be sought for in the vascular endothelium. The disease is transmissible, it attacks the same person but once, and always presents in its phenomena a regular order comparable with that observed in the eruptive fevers, all of which circumstances suggested to my mind the hypothesis that yellow fever should be considered a sort of eruptive fever in which the seat of the eruption is the vascular endothelium. The first period would correspond to the initial fever, the remission to the eruptive period, and the third period to that of desquamation. If the latter phase is accomplished under favourable conditions, the patient will only show evidence of an exaggerated transudation of some of the liquid elements of the blood through the new endothelium; if the conditions are unfavourable, a defective endothelium will have been produced, incapable of checking the escape of the figured elements of the blood; passive hæmorrhages will occur and the patient may find himself in imminent danger. Finally, assimilating the disease to smallpox and to vaccination, it occurred to me that in order to inoculate yellow fever it would be necessary to pick out the inoculable material from within the blood vessels of a yellow fever patient and to carry it likewise into the interior of a blood vessel of the person who was to be inoculated. All of which conditions the mosquito satisfies most admirably through its bite, in a manner which it would be almost impossible for us to imitate, with the comparatively coarse instruments which the most skilful makers could produce.

Three conditions will, therefore, be necessary in order that yellow fever may be propagated: (1) The existence of a yellow fever patient into whose capillaries the mosquito is able to drive its sting and to impregnate it with the virulent particles, at an appropriate stage of the disease. (2) That the life of the mosquito may be spared after its bite upon the patient until it has a chance of biting the person in whom the disease is to be reproduced. (3) The coincidence that some of the persons whom the same mosquito happens to bite thereafter shall be susceptible of contracting the disease.

Dr. Finlay continued to keep the subject in view, and he made a number of valuable contributions to it during the next ten or fifteen years, although as time advanced his ideas underwent some modification. His original theory, based on the studies made by Theobald Smith on Texas fever, was that the specific poison adhered to the mosquito's proboscis and was thus mechanically transferred to the individual next bitten, but he changed this view "so as to include the important circumstance that the faculty of transmitting the yellow fever germ need not be limited to the parent insect, directly contaminated by stinging a yellow fever patient, (or perhaps by constant contact with or feeding

from his discharges,) but may be likewise inherited
by the next generation of mosquitoes issued from
the contaminated parent." He also claimed, as
time went on, that the specific cause of the disease
was the *micrococcus tetragenus*.

During the years following Finlay's first contribution the ætiology of yellow fever was much
before the minds of scientists. After the brilliant
results in the causation of disease obtained by Koch
and Pasteur, bacteriologists naturally looked upon
yellow fever as a promising field for exploration.
In 1885 Dr. Domingo Freire of Rio de Janeiro
claimed to have found its specific cause in an organism which he named " *Cryptococcus zantho-
genicus.*" He obtained such favourable results
from inoculating human beings with attenuated
cultures of this organism for the purpose of con-
ferring immunity that he received a grant from
the state to enable him to continue his investigations. The work attracted considerable attention,
and he continued to report favourable results until
1887, when Dr. Sternberg of the United States
Army was sent to Rio de Janeiro for the purpose of
investigating into and reporting upon the merits
of the inoculations. Dr. Sternberg's report, however, was not encouraging, for he found that the
cultures made over to him by Freire for examination did not agree with the published descriptions

of his organism; moreover, the organism itself proved to be the common *staphylococcus pyogenes albus.*

Dr. Carmona y Valle of Mexico, in 1885, published the description of an organism which he considered to be the cause of yellow fever, but his claim, as well as that of Dr. Finlay for the *micrococcus tetragenus,* were disposed of by Dr. Sternberg, who showed that both these bacteria were common organisms that could be obtained from various sources. In 1888 Sternberg began an examination of the blood in yellow fever cases in Havana, investigating both blood from different organs and the contents of the intestinal tract, but without result, for, in his final report, he stated that the specific agent of the disease had not been demonstrated.

The ætiology of yellow fever remained, therefore, an undiscovered country. The knowledge of the disease acquired during a century of its more or less disastrous visitations amounted to very little. The old idea that the disease was spontaneously generated from organic decomposition under favorable conditions had, of course, died a natural death with the development of bacteriology as a science, and it was universally regarded as an importation. The old theory of contagion, which had been the subject of such heated controversy early in the nineteenth century, appeared at its close under a new form. Direct transmission from one person to another through the emanations from the body was no longer accredited, but its place was taken by the doctrine of *fomites,* which was supposed to afford a full explanation of its means of conveyance and to account satisfactorily for its transmission over great distances. The idea of studying the disease from the standpoint of its transportal had as yet occurred to no one but Dr. Finlay, and the scientific world in general was occupied in a search for the specific agent which, it was assumed, must be discovered before the nature of the disease could be satisfactorily investigated.

Such was the condition of knowledge, or rather of ignorance, concerning yellow fever when Dr. Reed took up the problem.

CHAPTER VI

WORK IN YELLOW FEVER
1897-1901

Dream not helm nor harness
    The sign of Valor true;
Peace hath higher test of manhood
    Than battle ever knew.
                    —WHITTIER. *The Hero.*

THE British Medical Journal for July 3, 1897, contained the announcement that, during the preceding year, the specific cause of yellow fever had been discovered by the Italian scientist, Dr. Giuseppe Sanarelli, in the form of a bacillus named by him *bacillus icteroides.* This statement was received with great interest by the scientific world, and by no one more gladly than Dr. Reed, who expressed the hope that Sanarelli's work would soon be confirmed by other observers. Shortly afterwards Reed himself, together with Dr. James Carroll, U. S. A., was appointed by Surgeon-General Sternberg to investigate Sanarelli's bacillus and compare it with the *bacillus x,* which Sternberg had obtained from the bodies of yellow fever patients during the summer of 1887. The investigation was begun with the desire on the part of the workers, as they themselves state, of confirming Sanarelli's observations. Their work, however, as it proceeded, revealed such strong structural resemblances between the *bacillus icteroides* and the *bacillus of hog-cholera* that it was determined to institute a different line of research, which soon convinced them that Sanarelli's bacillus was really a variety of the hog-cholera bacillus, and that if it was present in yellow fever at all, it must be regarded as a secondary invader.

The results of their investigation were formally expressed by Reed and Carroll in a "preliminary note," published in the Medical News for April 29, 1899;[1] Sanarelli challenged it four months later in the same journal,[2] denying the truth of the statements made by Reed and Carroll, explaining their failure to confirm his results by their employment of faulty methods, and even accusing them of lending themselves to the support of a personal controversy between himself and General Sternberg. Reed and Carroll replied to this attack without loss of time, showing beyond any possibility of doubt that Sanarelli's hostile criticisms of their

[1] "Bacillus icteroides and bacillus choleræ suis—A Preliminary Note." Med. News, April 29, 1899.

[2] "Some Observations and Controversial Remarks on the Specific Cause of Yellow Fever." Med. News, Aug. 12, 1899.

work were without foundation, and meeting his personal innuendoes with gentlemanly forbearance.[3] In December, 1900, they were able to publish the complete report of their investigations, which supplied overwhelming experimental proof that the *bacillus icteroides* belongs to the hog-cholera group.[4]

Before the appearance of this complete report, however, additional evidence in support of Reed and Carroll's results had been supplied through the investigations of Dr. Aristides Agramonte, Assistant Surgeon, U. S. A., who, during 1898 had studied the *bacillus icteroides* and the *bacillus x* in Dr. Reed's laboratory, and was then sent to Cuba, where he succeeded in isolating Sanarelli's bacillus from about thirty-three per cent. of the yellow fever cases examined at Santiago, but also obtained it from cases that were not yellow fever.

Early in the year 1900, yellow fever appeared among the American troops stationed at Havana, and became quite prevalent during the summer. In order to take advantage of this opportunity for investigating the ætiology of the disease, a com-

[3] "The Specific Cause of Yellow Fever." A Reply to Dr. G. Sanarelli. Med. News, Sept. 9, 1899.

[4] "A Comparative Study of the Biological Characters and Pathogenesis of Bacillus x (Sternberg), Bacillus icteroides (Sanarelli), and the Hog-Cholera Bacillus (Salmon and Smith)." Jour. Exper. Med., 1900, vol. V, p. 215.

mission of medical officers from the United States was appointed and ordered to meet at Havana for the purpose. The officers composing the board were: Dr. Walter Reed, Dr. James Carroll, and Dr. Jesse W. Lazear, all non-immunes, and Dr. Aristides Agramonte, a Cuban immune. Dr. Agramonte and Dr. Lazear were already in Cuba and Dr. Reed and Dr. Carroll joined them at Havana in June, 1900.

The work of the Commission was divided among its members as follows: Dr. Reed, the chairman, was at the head of affairs; Dr. Carroll had charge of the bacteriological investigations; Dr. Lazear had the mosquito work, for he was, at that time, the only member of the board acquainted with the mosquito; and Dr. Agramonte was in charge of the autopsies and of the pathological work.

The first efforts of the Commission were directed to a conclusive experiment on the true nature of the *bacillus icteroides*. For this purpose cultures drawn during life from the blood of eighteen patients were carefully studied, but as the *bacillus icteroides* could not be obtained from any of them, nor from cultures made at eleven autopsies on yellow fever patients, it was considered established beyond all doubt that it might be excluded from farther consideration.

Two separate lines of work now presented themselves: one, the study of the bacterial flora of the intestine and anerobic cultures from the blood and various organs of yellow fever patients; the other, the transmission of the disease according to the theory of insect conveyance advanced by Dr. Finlay, in 1881.

It happened that just at this time an opportunity was afforded Dr. Reed to investigate an epidemic of yellow fever prevailing at Pinar del Rio Barracks, about one hundred and two miles from Havana. In company with Dr. Agramonte, Dr. Reed made a visit there on July 31, 1900, and performed an autopsy on a yellow fever patient that afternoon. . . . His own description of the visit and the conclusions he drew from it are as follows:[5]

The lesions found were those of yellow fever. Inquiry showed that under the diagnosis of " remittent malarial fever," or "pernicious malarial fever," the disease had been prevailing for at least thirty-seven days prior to our arrival, July 31, and that about thirty-five cases had been under treatment in the post hospital, of which number eleven had died. As the true nature of the disease had not been suspected, no precautionary measures had been taken as regards the disinfection of bedding and clothing used by the patients, except that in case of death, the sheets and pillow slips were put into bichloride solution and the mattress and pillow

[5] " The Propagation of Yellow Fever; Observations based on recent Researches." Med. Rec., Aug. 10, 1901.

exposed to sunlight. An order required that the excreta of all patients under treatment in this hospital should be carefully disinfected, and this was probably carried out fairly well. . . . Notwithstanding the omission to disinfect the bulk of the contaminated articles of bedding and clothing, the disease had not been contracted by the nurses, nor by the three men who washed all of these articles. A little inquiry showed that contaminated clothing was in all of the eight barrack-rooms without apparent detriment to the occupants. Further investigation showed that a death from yellow fever had occurred in this garrison as early as May 16, 1900, and that the source of infection for this case, as well as for the present outbreak, was in the immediately adjacent town of Pinar del Rio, to which the soldiers had free access.

An interesting observation was the sudden attack of yellow fever experienced on July 12, 1900, by a general prisoner who had been confined in a cell in the guard house since June 6, 1900. His death occurred at the post hospital on July 18, 1900. This cell was occupied, at the time, by eight other prisoners, none of whom contracted the disease, although one of them continued to occupy the bunk vacated by the sick man. As these nine prisoners had been kept under strict military guard, it was impossible that the individual attacked could have acquired his infection in the town of Pinar del Rio. He was, as far as could be ascertained, exposed to no source of infection to which his companions had not been equally exposed, and yet he alone acquired the disease. *It was conjectured at the time that, perhaps, some insect capable of conveying the infection, such as the mosquito, had entered through the cell window, bitten this particular prisoner, and then passed out again. This, however, was only a supposition.*

Two instances of undoubted exposure to fomites involving four individuals came under my observation during this inspection. In the one case a box of clothing belonging to a soldier who had died of yellow fever on July 3, and which had been packed by an enlisted man on July 4 and placed in the company store-room, was unpacked for the purpose of making an inventory of the articles, and carefully repacked on July 18 by two non-immune soldiers, who did not contract the disease by this exposure. In the other case, the very bed vacated on July 18 by the Commissary Sergeant, who was taken sick on July 17, and died on July 21, was occupied by a non-immune soldier on the night of the 19th and 20th of July. Although this individual was badly frightened when the true character of the sergeant's attack was announced, the combination of fright and exposure to fomites was not sufficient to produce an attack of yellow fever.

It happened that Dr. Reed had been much impressed by the valuable observations made at Orwood and Taylor, Mississippi, during the year 1898 by Surgeon Henry R. Carter of the U. S. Marine Hospital Service, on the interval between infecting and secondary cases of yellow fever.[6] The circumstances under which Carter worked were favourable for recording the time between the

[6] New Orleans Med. Jour., May, 1900.

arrival of infecting cases, in isolated farmhouses, and the occurrence of secondary cases in these houses. According to him, "The period from the first (infecting) case to the first group of cases infected at these houses is generally from two to three weeks. The houses having become infected, susceptible individuals who visited them for a few hours fell sick with the disease in the usual period of incubation—one to seven days." Observations made by the Commission confirmed Carter's conclusions, and pointed, in Dr. Reed's opinion, to the presence of an intermediate host, such as the mosquito, which having taken the parasite into its stomach soon after the entrance of the patient into a non-infected house, was able after a certain interval to reconvey the infecting agent to other individuals. This interval appeared to be from nine to sixteen days (allowing for the period of incubation).

All these data induced Dr. Reed to form the following opinion:[7]

At this stage of our investigation, it seemed to me, and I so expressed the opinion to my colleagues, that the time had arrived when the plan of our work should be radically changed and that the search for the specific agent of yellow fever, while not abandoned, should

[7] "The Propagation of Yellow Fever: Observations Based on Recent Researches." *Loc. cit.*

be given secondary consideration, until we had first definitely learned something about the way or ways in which the disease was propagated from the sick to the well. I felt well-nigh convinced that we could obtain no light whatever upon the task that had been set before us, unless we substituted this line of work for the one we had been pursuing, and that in view of the splendid work of Ross, Bignami, and others with regard to the propagation of malarial fever, together with the well-known thermal influences intimately connected not only with the epidemiology of the disease in the United States, but also with its endemiology on the Island of Cuba, it was of the highest importance that the agency of an intermediate host, such as the mosquito, should either be proven or disproven.

" Notwithstanding the fact," Dr. Reed remarks elsewhere, " that Finlay had no results to show in support of his theory, and that the latter had been rejected by other investigators, the argument in favour of an intermediate host seemed so strong, as I have already said, that investigation along this line was determined upon."

The mosquito selected was that used by Finlay, and spoken of by him as *Culex fasciatus*. Culex, however, is an old genus, named by Linnæus in 1735, which for a long time contained all the mosquitoes. But other genera have been erected, and now the mosquitoes are included in a family known as the Culicidæ, which comprises several genera and very many species. Culex, however, is the typical genus and includes the commoner, most abundant, and most widespread kinds of mosquitoes. The particular species of mosquito used by Dr. Finlay in his original experiments is the one referred to in this country as *Culex fasciatus, Fabricius;* but Mr. F. V. Theobald, who has been investigating the mosquitoes of the world, on behalf of the British Museum, and has made a morphological study of these insects, has decided that *Culex fasciatus* is not to be contained in the genus Culex, but on account of scale structure and other structural peculiarities it must be placed in another genus, which has received the name *Stegomyia.* It is the female of one particular species, *Stegomyia fasciata,* which Dr. Reed made use of in his experiments upon yellow fever, and which, as we shall presently see, he demonstrated to be the intermediate host for the parasite of the disease.

The malarial mosquito (see Chapter V., p. 112) belongs to another genus, namely, *Anopheles,* founded by Meigen in 1818. There are three species of Anopheles in the United States: A. *maculipennis* Meigen, A. *punctipennis* Say, and A. *crucians* Wied. It is not known whether the insect was introduced from Europe to America or the reverse. It is quite within the bounds of possibility that malaria was originally an European disease, and that not only was the disease itself carried from there on sailing vessels, but the mosquito which propagated it as well—at any rate to America.

The following description of *Stegomyia fasciata,* its appearance, habitat, and breeding places is abridged from Dr. Reed's account of it:

This mosquito is rather a striking looking insect. It has conspicuous markings of a broad, semilunar, silvery stripe on the lateral surface of the thorax, and white stripes at the bases of the tarsal joints. Four stripes of silvery scales seen on the posterior surface of the thorax distinguish this species from all others, except *Stegomyia signifer*. It has a widespread distribution, being found in all the principal cities of Cuba, as well as in almost all the southern countries of Europe, and the Southern States of this country. Its breeding places are in rainwater barrels or sagging gutters containing water, and indeed in all places where stagnant water has collected. The female lays her eggs during the night, extruding them on the surface of the water in pairs, in groups of three or more, or singly. The number of eggs deposited varies from twenty to about seventy-five. They are jet black in colour and, to the naked eye, cylindrical in shape. Under a low power of the microscope the surface of the egg is seen to be marked by tolerably regular six-sided plates, each of which has a little round elevation in the centre, that gives the surface a roughened appearance. The eggs are singularly resistant to external influences. Dried eggs can be easily hatched at the end of three months

and freezing does not destroy their fertility. The eggs
are laid after a meal of blood after an interval varying
from two to thirty days—as a rule within seven days—
and under favourable conditions of warmth (*i. e.,* a
summer temperature) they begin to hatch on the third
day. The larval stage occupies seven to eight days and
the pupal stage about two days. The impregnated
female bites at a temperature of 62° F. and above, but
at a lower temperature even very hungry females will
not bite; the unimpregnated female does not appear
to bite at all. Unlike *culex pungens,* this mosquito bites
by day as well as by night. [8]

The line of work being finally determined, there
at once arose the tremendous responsibility involved in the use of human beings for experimental
purposes. After careful consideration the Commission reached the conclusion that the results, if
positive, would be of sufficient service to humanity
to justify the procedure, provided, of course, that
each individual subjected to experiment was fully
informed of the risks he ran, and gave his free consent. The members of the Commission, however,
agreed that it was their duty to run the risk involved themselves, before submitting anyone else
to it.

It became necessary just at this time for Dr.

[8] "The Prevention of Yellow Fever." Med. Rec., Oct. 26,
1901.

Reed to return to this country, and the work was left in charge of Dr. Carroll. The experiments were begun by Dr. Lazear, who applied a number of infected mosquitoes, hatched from eggs furnished by Dr. Finlay, to several persons, himself included, without result. On the afternoon of August 27 a second attempt was made, in which Dr. Carroll submitted to the bite of an infected mosquito, applied by Dr. Lazear. The description of this, the first successful experiment, is best given in Dr. Carroll's own words.[9]

The insect, which had been hatched and reared in the laboratory, had been caused to feed upon four cases of yellow fever, two of them severe and two mild. The first patient, a severe case, was bitten twelve days before, the second, third, and fourth patients had been bitten six, four, and two days previously, and their attacks were in character, mild, severe, and mild, respectively. In writing to Dr. Reed on the night after the incident I remarked jokingly that if there were anything in the mosquito theory I should have a good dose; and so it happened. After having slight premonitory symptoms for two days I was taken sick on August 31, and on September 1 I was carried to the yellow fever camp. My life was in the balance for three days, and my chart shows that on the fifth, sixth,

[9] " A Brief Review of the Etiology of Yellow Fever." N. Y. Med. Jour. and Phil. Med. Jour. (consol.), Feb. 6 and 13, 1904.

and seventh days my urine contained eight-tenths and nine-tenths of moist albumen. The tests were made by Dr. Lazear. I mention this particularly because the results obtained in this case do not agree with the twentieth conclusion of Marchoux, Salimbeni, and Simond, that the longer the interval that elapses after infection of the mosquito the more dangerous he becomes. Twelve days, the period above cited, is the shortest time in which the mosquito has been proved to be capable of conveying the infection. It is my opinion that the susceptibility of the individual bitten is a much more potent factor in determining the severity of the attack than the duration of the infection in the mosquito, or the number of mosquitoes applied. On the day that I was taken sick, August 31, 1900, Dr. Lazear applied the same mosquito, with three others, to another individual who suffered a comparatively mild attack, and was well before I left my bed. Thus it happened that I was the first person to whom the mosquito was proved to convey the disease. On the eighteenth day of September, five days after I was permitted to leave my bed, Dr. Lazear was stricken and died in convulsions just one week later, after several days of delirium with black vomit. Such is yellow fever.

As soon as Dr. Carroll fell ill, Dr. Lazear applied the insects which had bitten him, together with three others, to another subject mentioned in the report as X. Y., who also succumbed to the disease after the usual period of incubation. In doing this Lazear was actuated by the scientific spirit, for he confirmed the source of infection in Dr. Carroll's case, while at the same time he secured additional proof regarding the transmission of the disease by the mosquito. The entire series of pre- liminary experiments consisted of eleven cases, nine of which were negative; it was felt, however, that the negative results might be attributed to the fact that the insects used in them had not been kept long enough after biting yellow fever patients. The two positive cases were therefore considered sufficiently encouraging to justify advancing along the line of investigation already proposed, espe- cially as the movements of both patients in the suc- cessful cases were known to the Commission for some weeks prior to their inoculation, and gave reasonable assurance that no other source of infec- tion had been possible.

The death of Dr. Lazear, mentioned by Dr. Carroll, occurred in consequence of an accidental inoculation. He had been experimentally bitten, as I have said above, without any result, but a short time afterwards a mosquito settled on his hand while he was collecting blood from a yellow fever patient for purposes of investigation, and he allowed it to take its fill. He did not at the time believe it to belong to the species *stegomyia,* and said nothing about the occurrence to his associates. In due course of time, however, he was taken ill with yellow fever in its most virulent form, and died within a week. His death was an irreparable loss to the Commission, but I will not pause here to dwell on his many claims to admiration and respect, for I shall speak of them at length in their own time and place (see Chapter XI).

Dr. Reed returned to find the first series of experiments, upon which the utility of the mosquito theory as a working hypothesis must rest, already accomplished through the exertions of his colleagues, and the Preliminary Note for publication was immediately begun. As Lazear's infection was accidental, his case is not officially cited in the report, though it is mentioned incidentally; but, as the bite was received while he was actually in the yellow fever ward, the presumptive evidence in favor of his infection through the mosquito is very strong. The two positive cases, however, were considered by the Commission sufficient evidence to justify them in stating before the Public Health Association at Indianapolis in October, 1900, that " *The mosquito acts as the intermediate host for the parasite of yellow fever.*" [10]

The first stage in the investigation thus completed, it became evident that, if further experiments were to be of permanent value to humanity, some means must be provided by which perfect

[10] "The Etiology of Yellow Fever: A Preliminary Note." Address before the American Health Assoc., Indianapolis, Oct., 1900.

control could be exercised over the movements of the individuals subjected to inoculation, in order to exclude every possible source of infection except the mosquito. An experimental sanitary station was, therefore, established, in an open, uncultivated field, about one mile from the town of Quemados, Cuba, on a site which was well drained and freely exposed to both sun and wind. This station, which was named Camp Lazear in memory of the deceased member of the Commission, was placed under Dr. Reed's entire control, and he speaks of it thus: [11]

Any location selected, provided it should be one mile from such a centre of infection and surrounded by proper safeguards, would be just as free from the occurrence of yellow fever as if it were located ten miles from such a town. My own experience on the Island of Cuba had already taught me that yellow fever could be easily kept out of a military garrison, although prevailing in epidemic form in a town less than one mile distant. For this reason it was not considered advisable to establish our experimental sanitary station at a greater distance than one mile from Quemados, Cuba. Thus Camp Lazear could easily be reached by the members of the Board and was conveniently located as regards its basis of supplies.

The personnel of the camp, in addition to the three surviving members of the Commission, con-

[11] " The Propagation of Yellow Fever." Med. Record, Aug. 10, 1901.

CAMP LAZEAR

where the experiments with the yellow fever mosquito were first carried
out and the transmission of the disease by this means proven

sisted of Dr. Roger P. Ames, an immune, in immediate charge; Dr. Robert P. Cooke, a non-immune; one acting hospital steward, an immune;
nine privates of the hospital corps, one of whom
was an immune; and one immune ambulance
driver.

For the quartering of this detachment and of
such non-immune individuals as should be received
for experimentation, hospital tents, properly
floored, were provided, placed at about twenty feet
apart and numbered 1 to 7 respectively. Camp
Lazear was established on November 20, 1900, and
from this date was put under strict quarantine, no
one being permitted to leave or enter camp, except
the three immune members of the detachment.
Supplies were drawn chiefly from Columbia Barracks, and for this purpose a conveyance under the
control of the immune acting hospital steward, and
having an immune driver, was used. A few Spanish immigrants, recently arrived at Havana, were
received from time to time, but a non-immune
person having once left the camp was not permitted
to return under any circumstances whatever. The
temperature and pulse of all non-immune residents
were carefully recorded three times daily, so that
any infected individual entering the camp could
be promptly detected and removed. No non-immune resident was subjected to inoculation who

had not passed in this camp the full period of incubation of yellow fever with one exception, for which there was a special reason.[12]

It was now proposed [says Dr. Reed], to attempt the infection of non-immune individuals in three different ways, namely, first, by the bites of mosquitoes which had previously bitten cases of yellow fever; second, by the injection of blood taken during the early stages from the general circulation of those suffering the disease; and third, by exposure to the most intimate contact with fomites. For this purpose, in addition to the seven tents provided for the quartering of the detachment, two frame buildings each 14x20 feet in size were constructed. These buildings, having a capacity of 2800 feet, were exactly similar, except that one of them, known as the " Infected Mosquito Building," was divided near the middle by a permanent wire screen partition and had good ventilation; while the other, designated as the " Infected Clothing Building," was purposely so constructed as to exclude anything like efficient ventilation. These houses were placed on opposite sides of a small valley, about eighty yards apart, and each seventy-five yards distant from the camp proper. Both houses were provided with wire screen windows and double wire screen doors, so that mosquitoes could be kept within or without the buildings as the experimenters might desire.[13]

[12] " Etiology of Yellow Fever: An Additional Note." Jour. Amer. Med. Assoc., Feb. 16, 1901.
[13] " Propagation of Yellow Fever." Loc. cit.

The subject of the first experiment was a young private from Ohio, named John R. Kissinger, who volunteered for the service, to use his own words, "solely in the interest of humanity and the cause of science." When it became known among the troops that subjects were needed for experimental purposes, Kissinger, in company with another young private named John J. Moran, also from Ohio, volunteered their services. Dr. Reed talked the matter over with them, explaining fully the danger and suffering involved in the experiment should it be successful, and then, seeing they were determined, he stated that a definite money compensation would be made them. Both young men declined to accept it, making it, indeed, their sole stipulation that they should receive no pecuniary reward, whereupon Major Reed touched his cap, saying respectfully, "Gentlemen, I salute you." Reed's own words in his published account of the experiment on Kissinger, are: "In my opinion this exhibition of moral courage has never been surpassed in the annals of the Army of the United States."

It should be mentioned to the credit of the United States Army that when men were needed for duty in different capacities at Camp Lazear, the number of volunteers was always in excess of the demand. Subjects for experiment by inoculation or by exposure to fomites were always forth-coming of their own choice, although no pains were spared by those in command to make them fully understand the risks they assumed.

On December 5, 1900, at 2 P. M., five promising mosquitoes were selected, two of which had been contaminated fifteen days previously; one, nine-teen days; and two, twenty-two days. These were allowed, with his free consent, to bite the patient, John R. Kissinger; the result of the bites was per-fectly successful, for about midnight on December 8, at the end of three days, nine and a half hours, the subject, who had been under strict quarantine during fifteen days, was seized with a chill that proved the beginning of a well-marked attack of yellow fever.

Dr. Reed watched the progress of this case with intense interest, and wrote to his wife concerning it as follows:

COLUMBIA BARRACKS, QUEMADOS, CUBA.
Dec. 9, 1900.

It is with a great deal of pleasure that I hasten to tell you that we have succeeded in producing a case of unmistakable yellow fever by the bite of the mosquito. Our first case in the experimental camp developed at 11.30 last night, commencing with a sudden chill fol-lowed by fever. He had been bitten at 11.30,[14] Dec.

---

[14] Probably a *lapsus pennæ* for 2.30, which is the time stated in the published record.

5th, and hence his attack followed just three and a half days after the bite. As he had been in our camp 15 days before being inoculated and had had no other possible exposure, the case is as clear as the sun at noon-day, and sustains brilliantly and conclusively our conclusions. Thus, just 18 days from the time we began our experimental work we have succeeded in demonstrating this mode of propagation of the disease, so that the most doubtful and sceptical must yield. Rejoice with me, sweetheart, as, aside from the antitoxin of diphtheria and Koch's discovery of the tubercle bacillus, it will be regarded as the most important piece of work, scientifically, during the 19th century. I do not exaggerate, and I could shout for very joy that heaven has permitted me to establish this wonderful way of propagating yellow fever. It was Finlay's theory, and he deserves great credit for having suggested it, but as he did nothing to prove it, it was rejected by all, including General Sternberg. Now we have put it beyond cavil, and its importance to Cuba and the United States cannot be estimated. Major Kean says that the discovery is worth more than the cost of the Spanish War, including lives lost and money expended. He is almost beside himself with joy and will tell General Wood when he goes to town in the morning. To-morrow afternoon we will have the Havana Board of Experts, Drs. Guiteras, Albertini, and Finlay, come out and diagnose the case. I shan't tell them how the infection was acquired until after they have satisfied themselves concerning the character of the case, then I will let them know. I suppose that old Dr. Finlay will be delighted beyond bounds, as he will see his theory at last fully vindicated. 9.30 P. M. Since writing the above our patient has been doing well. His temperature, which was 102.5° at noon, has fallen to 101° and his severe headache and backache have subsided considerably. Everything points, as far as it can at this stage, to a favourable termination, for which I feel so happy.

Two days later he writes:

Dec. 11, 1900.

Our patient, concerning whom I wrote you in my last, is doing very well. We had Dr. John Guiteras, Dr. Finlay, and Dr. Albertini out here to see him yesterday afternoon. They were all immensely interested and Dr. Albertini did not hesitate to say "yellow fever." The others too regarded the case as one of probable yellow fever, but desired to see how his temperature and pulse would run during the next few days. Dr. Amador, an expert in yellow fever, says the disease is undoubtedly yellow fever. Of course, I can't blame anyone from withholding a diagnosis until they are satisfied, but from my standpoint it is very amusing. The case is as plain as the nose on a man's face, but as Dr. —— has pronounced in an interview our theory as being very "wild and improbable," of course he wants to be "let down easy," for he must surrender. He will come round in a few days. Dr. Gorgas also saw the patient and pronounced the case as so suspicious that had it occurred in Havana he would not have hesitated to send him to the yellow fever hospital. Ah! wonderful is nature, and I thank God that he has allowed poor unworthy me to look a little way into this secret. Six months ago, when we landed on this island, absolutely nothing was known concerning the propagation and spread of yellow fever—it was all an unfathomable mystery—but to-day the curtain has been drawn—its mode of propagation is established and we know that a case minus mosquitoes is no more dangerous than one of chills and fever! Hurrah! I will write to Dr. —— in a few days about the case. Of course he will at once write an article to say that for 20 years he has considered the mosquito as the most probable cause of yellow fever. That would be just in order for him to do. Dr. —— of the Marine Service has written a very discourteous reply to our Preliminary Note in the same Journal that our article appeared in. . . . Dr. Cobb, of the same service, has also written a very courteous and interesting answer to our paper, in which he proves to his own satisfaction that the mosquito can't possibly propagate the disease, and says that it would be dreadful after all the years of disinfection that his service has done if this theory should be what we have claimed for it. And so the ball rolls on!

During the week following the onset of Kissinger's attack four other cases of yellow fever were produced by inoculation with mosquitoes, and this further confirmation of the mosquito theory had one somewhat amusing effect, which Dr. Reed describes thus: [15]

It can readily be imagined that the occurrence of four cases of yellow fever in our small command of twelve non-immunes, within the space of one week,

[15] " Propagation of Yellow Fever: Observations Based on Recent Researches." *Loc. cit.*

while giving rise to feelings of exultation in the hearts of the experimenters, in view of the vast importance attaching to these results, might inspire quite other sentiments in the bosoms of those who had previously consented to submit themselves to the mosquito's bite. In fact, several of our good-natured Spanish friends, who had jokingly compared our mosquitoes to " the little flies that buzzed harmlessly about their tables," suddenly appeared to lose all interest in the progress of science, and forgetting for the moment even their own personal aggrandisement, incontinently severed their connection with Camp Lazear. Personally, while lamenting, to some extent, their departure, I could not but feel that in placing themselves beyond our control they were exercising the soundest judgment. In striking contrast to the want of confidence shown by these Andalusians, who had agreed to be bitten by the mosquitoes, was the conduct now displayed by the three young Americans who had consented to jeopardise their lives by exposure to fomites, and who, as a matter of fact, had already passed fifteen nights in a small ill-ventilated building, breathing in an atmosphere dreadfully contaminated by the soiled garments of yellow fever patients. With the occurrence of these cases of mosquito infection the countenances of these men, which had before borne the serious aspect of those who were bravely facing an unseen foe, suddenly took on the glad expression of school-boys let out for a holiday, and from this time their contempt for " fomites " could not find sufficient expression. Thus illustrating once more the old adage that familiarity, even with fomites, may breed contempt!

The experiments regarding infection with fomites, here alluded to, formed an essential part of Dr. Reed's work, since it was nearly as important to establish the fact that yellow fever could not be conveyed in this way as to prove that it could be transmitted by the mosquito. To show that the mosquito was responsible for the transmission of yellow fever, without disproving its conveyance by fomites, would only have added to the confusion and dread with which the whole subject of the disease was surrounded. For many years it had been unhesitatingly accepted that the epidemics which devastated the country had their origin in the unpacking of boxes and trunks containing infected clothing; hence the efforts of the health authorities were constantly directed to the disinfection of clothing and bedding from ports where yellow fever prevailed.

To determine whether clothing contaminated by contact with yellow fever patients or their discharges really conveyed the disease from one person or one place to another became, therefore, a matter of vital importance. If the mosquito theory was true, the fomites theory had no foundation, but nothing short of actual demonstration of its futility could be relied on to induce conviction.

One of the frame buildings erected at Camp Lazear had been designed for the special purpose of conducting this series of experiments. It con-

sisted of one room, 14 x 20 feet in size, with two
tiny windows both facing south, and closed with
wire screens, so that a thorough circulation of air
was impossible; in addition there were glass sashes
within and heavy wooden shutters without, the
latter being intended for the purpose of excluding
the sunlight. Entrance was through a small vesti-
bule on the same side as the windows, protected
without by a solid door and divided in the middle
by a wire screen door. The inner entrance had also
a screen door, and in this way the entrance of mosquitoes was effectually prevented. This house was
kept closed till long after sunset and was heated to
a temperature of 92° to 95° F. with precautions to
secure sufficient humidity.

On November 30 [says Dr. Reed], the building being
now ready for occupation, three large boxes filled with
sheets, pillowslips, blankets, etc., contaminated by contact with cases of yellow fever and their discharges, were
received and placed there. The majority of the articles
had been taken from the beds of patients sick with yellow
fever at Las Animas Hospital, Havana, or at Columbia Barracks. Many of them had been purposely soiled
with a liberal quantity of black vomit, urine, and fecal
matter. A dirty " comfortable " and much-soiled pair
of blankets, removed from the bed of a patient sick
with yellow fever in the town of Quemados, were contained in one of these boxes. The same day at 6 P. M.
Dr. Robert P. Cooke, Acting Assistant Surgeon, U. S.

CAMP LAZEAR

Building where the experiments were made which proved that yellow fever is not transmitted by means of infected clothing (fomites). The figure on the left is Dr. Carroll.

A., and two privates of the hospital corps, Folk and Jernigan, all non-immune young Americans, entered this building and deliberately unpacked these boxes, which had been tightly closed and locked for a period of two weeks. They were careful at the same time to give each article a thorough handling and shaking in order to disseminate through the air of the room the specific agent of yellow fever, if contained in these fomites. These soiled sheets, pillow-cases, and blankets were used in preparing the beds in which the members of the hospital corps slept. Various soiled articles were hung around the room and placed about the bed occupied by Dr. Cooke.

From this date until December 19, a period of twenty days, this room was occupied each night by these three non-immunes. Each morning the various soiled articles were carefully packed in the aforesaid boxes, and at night again unpacked and distributed about the room. During the day the residents of this house were permitted to occupy a tent pitched in the immediate vicinity, but were kept in strict quarantine.

December 12 a fourth box of clothing and bedding was received from Las Animas Hospital. These articles had been used on the beds of yellow fever patients, but in addition had been purposely soiled with the bloody stools of a fatal case of the disease. As this box had been packed for a number of days, when it was opened and unpacked by Dr. Cooke and his assistants on December 12, the odour was so offensive as to compel them to retreat from the house. They pluckily returned, however, within a short time and spent the night as usual.

On December 19 these three non-immunes were placed in quarantine for five days, and then given the liberty of the camp. All had remained in perfect health, notwithstanding their stay of twenty nights amid such unwholesome surroundings.[16]

This experiment was repeated on three subsequent occasions, the only variation being that on several occasions the men actually slept in the garments used by yellow fever patients, and notwithstanding this trying ordeal, they continued in perfect health. There could be no doubt, therefore, that the attempt to convey the disease by means of fomites was a total failure, and if measures to convey disease, thus carried out, with every conceivable precaution against its entrance by other sources of infection and every conceivable facility for its admission by the sources under consideration came to no effect, the experiment might be accepted as unquestionable evidence that the disease is not conveyed by fomites. Dr. Reed writes to his wife on the subject as follows:

COLUMBIA BARRACKS,
Dec. 9, 1900.

I have allowed the men who have spent 20 nights in our infected clothing house to come out and they are now in quarantine. Two other soldiers are now occu-

[16] " The Etiology of Yellow Fever." *Loc. cit.*

pying the house and sleeping not only in the same beds and between the same sheets on which our yellow fever patients have rested during their attacks, *but they sleep in the very shirts that our patients wore throughout their entire illness!* If anything should give them the disease this should succeed! Don't you think so? Infected clothing and bedding have been a horrible nightmare during the past 300 years, but, methinks, it will die out very early in the next century! Yellow fever can no more be transmitted in that way than intermittent fever. How General Sternberg and hosts of others could have believed in the contagiousness of clothing and of the stools of yellow fever patients I cannot possibly see. They were simply accepting the statements of others who had nothing on which to base such statements. A little careful testing of this theory has served to knock it completely into smithereens. I thank God that I did not accept anybody's opinion on this subject, but determined to put it to a thorough test with human beings in order to see what would happen. My own observations at Pinar del Rio convinced me that infected bedding was indeed a myth. Actual trial has proven that I was right and that what the medical profession believed was wrong! '

It seems but just that we should pause a moment here to commend the courageous spirit of the men who submitted to the fomites experiments. Dr. Cooke, in a private letter, disclaims any credit for bravery, in the modest spirit which has distinguished all the men engaged in these researches;

but, while it is true that the risk of acquiring yellow fever in this way is absolutely *nil,* the fact was not established at the time the men began their sojourn in the infected clothing building. Apart, however, from any question of possible yellow fever, surely there can be no finer spirit of self-devotion to the cause of science and of humanity than that which voluntarily spends a considerable time amid such repulsive surroundings. To pass twenty nights in a small, ill-ventilated room, with the temperature over ninety, in close contact with the most loathsome articles of dress and furniture, in an atmosphere fetid from their presence, is an act of heroism which ought to command our highest admiration and our lasting gratitude.

The non-contagiousness of fomites being thus definitely settled, the question arose: How does a house become infected with yellow fever? and the next experiment undertaken was for the purpose of demonstrating that the essential factor in the infection of a building with yellow fever is the presence of mosquitoes that have bitten cases of the disease.

Accordingly [says Dr. Reed],[17] at 11.55, December 21, 1900, fifteen mosquitoes were freed in the larger room of the " Infected Mosquito Building "

[17] " The Propagation of Yellow Fever," etc. *Loc. cit.*

which, as I have said, was divided into two compartments by a wire-screen partition. The interval that had elapsed since the contamination of these insects was as follows: one, twenty-four days; three, twelve days; four, eight days; and seven, five days. The only articles of furniture in this building consisted of three beds, one being placed in the mosquito room and two beyond the wire screen, these latter intended to be occupied by two " control " non-immunes. The articles of bedding as well as the bedsteads had been carefully disinfected by steam. At noon on the same day, five minutes after the mosquitoes had been placed therein, a plucky Ohio boy, Moran by name,[18] clad only in his night-shirt and fresh from a bath, entered the room containing the mosquitoes, where he lay down for a period of thirty minutes. On the opposite side of the screen were the two "controls" and one other non-immune. Within two minutes after Moran's entrance he was bitten about the face and hands by the insects that had promptly settled down upon him. Seven in all bit him at this visit. At 4.30 P. M. he again entered and remained twenty minutes, during which time five others bit him. The following day at 4.30 P. M. he again entered and remained fifteen minutes, during which three insects bit him, making the number fifteen that fed at these three visits. The building was then closed, except that the two non-immune " controls " continued to occupy the beds on the non-infected side of the screen. On Christmas morning at 11 A. M. this brave lad was

[18] This young man, who volunteered at the same time as Kissinger, had already been the subject of one inoculation, immediately after that of Kissinger. The results in his case, however, had been negative.

stricken with yellow fever and had a sharp attack which he bore without a murmur. The period of incubation in this case was three days and twenty-three hours, counting from his first visit, or two days and seventeen and a half hours, if reckoned from his last visit. The two " controls " who had slept each night in this house, only protected by the wire screen, but breathing the common atmosphere of the building, had remained in good health. They continued to remain so, although required to sleep here for thirteen additional nights. As Moran had remained in strict quarantine for the period of thirty-two days prior to his attack, the source of his infection must be found in this house.

With this experiment the work for the time being came to a close. Dr. Reed's own sentiments regarding the blessing it had conferred upon the human race are expressed in the following letter to his wife:

COLUMBIA BARRACKS,
QUEMADOS, CUBA,
11.50 P. M., Dec. 31, 1900.

Only ten minutes of the old century remain. Here have I been sitting, reading that most wonderful book, " La Roche on Yellow Fever," written in 1853. Forty-seven years later it has been permitted to me and my assistants to lift the impenetrable veil that has surrounded the causation of this most wonderful, dreadful pest of humanity and to put it on a rational and scientific basis. I thank God that this has been accomplished during the latter days of the old century. May its cure be wrought out in the early days of the new! The prayer that has been mine for twenty years, that I might be permitted in some way or at some time to do something to alleviate human suffering has been granted! A thousand Happy New Years. . . . Hark, there go the twenty-four buglers in concert, all sounding " Taps " for the old year.

CHAPTER VII

WORK IN YELLOW FEVER (CONTINUED)

Thine the victory,
As the just Future measures gain.
—JAMES RUSSELL LOWELL.

THE new year opened auspiciously for the work of the Yellow Fever Commission. The members felt themselves justified in stating publicly that they had proved the transmission of yellow fever by means of the mosquito, as well as the harmlessness of fomites in conveying the disease; and they were gratified to find that the results were received with enthusiasm in Havana. Dr. Reed describes their reception in a letter to his wife, from which we have already quoted, as follows:

COLUMBIA BARRACKS, CUBA,
Dec. 23, 1900.

Last evening I attended quite a swell banquet in Havana given to Dr. Finlay by some seventy or eighty physicians of Havana. It was a very *recherché* affair and extremely enjoyable. Everything was in Spanish —the Governor General was there—the toasts were all in Spanish, and the speeches, while flattering to Dr.

154

Finlay for his conception of the theory, gave us full credit for the discovery. It is to me surprising and extremely satisfactory to see how very quickly the profession of Havana have accepted our results.

The work of the Commission was now nearly completed, and on January 1, 1901, Reed writes:

I celebrated the day by writing to General Sternberg, and requesting him to have the order for our return issued so that we could leave here the night after the close of the Pan-American Congress. Six weeks from to-day I hope to be at home again.

Before leaving Cuba, however, Dr. Reed wished to investigate some points of minor interest associated with the problems of moment which he had just solved, namely, *whether yellow fever could be transmitted by any other means than the bite of the mosquito,* and *what was the length of time during which the mosquito was capable of conveying the infection.* In order to determine the first question it was decided to try inoculation with the blood of a yellow fever patient, the Commission regarding it as probable that yellow fever, like the several types of malarial fever, might be produced by the injection of blood taken from a patient suffering with the disease.

The subject of the experiment was a non-immune private, named Jernigan, who has already been

mentioned as one of those who slept in the " Infected Clothing Building." He had been bitten by
an infected mosquito on December 28 and 29, 1900,
with negative results, but it was thought that the
failure of the experiment might possibly be due to
some degree of natural immunity, or, more probably, to the fact that as most of the mosquitoes first
used had been destroyed (presumably, by the small
red ants which abounded), those by which Jernigan
was bitten were only thirteen days old. While this
matter was still under discussion, an opportunity
to make a good inoculation presented itself, and
as Jernigan was the only available subject in the
camp, it was determined to make use of him for
the purpose. He was accordingly inoculated subcutaneously on January 4, 1901, with two cubic
centimetres of blood taken from the arm of a yellow fever patient twenty-four hours after the onset
of the disease; an attack of yellow fever developed
in a little less than four days, showing that although
the bite of the mosquito is the natural method for
the transmission of the disease, it is not essential.
It would also appear that the mosquito at certain
periods of the disease may fail to obtain the parasite, a result not unlike that sometimes found when
the blood is examined in malarial fever. This first
experiment was confirmed by three others, in which
the subcutaneous injection of blood gave positive

results, the amounts administered being 1.5, 0.5, and 1 cc., respectively. Dr. Reed's remarks on these experiments are as follows: [1]

The production of yellow fever in this way is of much scientific interest; first, as serving to confirm what the mosquito inoculation had already shown, *viz.*, that the parasite is present in the general circulation; second, that passage through the body of the mosquito, although this would seem to be nature's method, is not absolutely necessary in the life-history of this micro-organism; and third, that the period of incubation of the disease, when thus produced, corresponds fairly closely to that occasioned by the mosquito's bite. A point of considerable interest brought out by the blood injection was the absence from the blood, on careful bacteriologic culture, of any bacterium which grows on our ordinary media by anerobic methods; thus excluding absolutely the *bacillus icteroides* of Sanarelli from further claim as the specific agent of yellow fever.

The second point of interest, that is, the number of days which must elapse after contamination of the mosquito before it can convey the disease to a second individual, was now taken up.

After a quarantine period of nine days [Dr. Reed says],[2] a man named Martinez visited the room (in

[1] "The Propagation of Yellow Fever," etc. *Loc. cit.*
[2] "The Propagation of Local Fever." *Loc. cit.*

which the mosquitoes were now kept in jars) and there, on December 17, 1900, was bitten by fourteen mosquitoes, which four days before had fed upon the first case (Kissinger's). The result was quite negative, and on December 24, or on the *eleventh day* after contamination, the subject was again bitten by seven of these insects, all that remained of the original fourteen. Again no infection took place. After six full days, or on December 30, at 11 o'clock A. M., Martinez was again bitten by the surviving four of the mosquitoes, *i. e.,* on the *seventeenth* day after their contamination. On the fourth day thereafter, January 3, 1901, at 10.30 A. M., he was seized with yellow fever, which ran a typical course. The period of incubation was three days twenty-two and one-half hours.   Although we cannot say on what particular day these insects became capable of conveying the disease, we are able to state that they were incapable of infecting on the *fourth* or the *eleventh* day after contamination. These observations seem to indicate that after the parasite has been taken into the mosquito's stomach a certain number of days must elapse before the insect is capable of reconveying it to a second individual. This period probably represents the time required for the parasite to undergo its cycle of development and reach the mosquito's salivary glands; and, as far as our experience goes, the length of time is about twelve days in summer weather, and most probably about eighteen or more days during cooler winter months. The experiment just given, therefore, does not support the opinion of Finlay that the bite of the contaminated mosquito confers immunity against a subsequent attack of the disease, since we have seen that neither the bites of fourteen insects on the fourth day nor the bites of seven on the eleventh day after contamination, prevented, in the least, the conveyance of the infection by the bites of four only of these mosquitoes on the seventeenth day.

In the next case, the subject, an immune American, was bitten by insects that had fed upon the first case (Kissinger's) on the third day of his illness, that is, during the secondary fever, which in this case followed a complete intermission. These mosquitoes had been kept alive on sugar and water for a period of *thirty-nine days* before being applied to the case in question. Of the original five insects that had bitten Kissinger on the third day, four were still alive on the thirty-ninth day afterward, and three showed every evidence of good appetite. This particular subject, having passed twenty-one nights in the infected clothing building, during which time he was exposed to the most intimate contact with fomites without apparent detriment to his health, had been kept in strict quarantine for yet thirty days longer at Camp Lazear. At the expiration of this time, on January 19, 1901, at 4.30 P. M., he visited the mosquito-room, where he was bitten by these thirty-nine-day-old insects, three in number. This inoculation was followed by an attack of yellow fever of moderate severity, which began at 4 P. M. January 23, the period of incubation being three days and twenty-three and one-half hours.

The next case [says Dr. Reed],[3] is of equal interest, as the patient was infected in the same room by the bites of two of these same mosquitoes on the *fifty-first* day after their contamination, the period of incubation being three days and two and one-half hours, and the character of the attack mild; while still another case conclusively demonstrates that these identical insects, on the *fifty-seventh* day after their contamination, were not only capable of conveying the infection, but of producing an attack of such severity that the subject's life hung in the balance for several days. I regret to have to state that the individual who had consented to be bitten by these insects on the *sixty-second* day after their contamination failed to fulfil his promise at the last moment; otherwise I cannot say to what old age these mosquitoes might have attained. Deprived of further opportunity to feed on human blood, one died on the sixty-ninth day and the other on the seventy-first day after their original contamination. The duration of life in the case of these mosquitoes will readily explain how the poison of yellow fever can remain even in a depopulated area for a period of two and a half months, so that, as is well known, those who enter the infected area, even at the expiration of this period, are liable to acquire the disease.

The last successful case of mosquito infection at Camp Lazear was bitten on February 7, 1901, after

[3] " The Propagation of Yellow Fever." *Loc. cit.*

a period of twenty-five days' quarantine, by two mosquitoes, on the sixteenth day after their contamination, and was seized with an attack of yellow fever at
noon on February 10, after an incubation period of
two days and twenty-two hours.

These experiments, confirming those already
mentioned by Carter in 1898, enabled Dr. Reed to
state positively that at least twelve days must elapse
between contamination of the mosquito by the
blood of a yellow fever patient and the communication of the disease, while the period may be as
much as twenty-three. They also show that the
mosquito is capable of conveying the disease for a
period of fifty-seven days, and quite possibly
longer.

The Pan-American Congress met at Havana on
February 4-7, 1901, and Dr. Reed submitted before
it a paper describing his experiments and stating
his results. The points which he felt himself justified in publishing as proved are these:[4]

(1) The mosquito, *C. fasciatus,* serves as the intermediate host for the parasite of yellow fever.

(2) Yellow fever is transmitted to the non-immune
individual by means of the bite of the mosquito that has
previously fed on the blood of those sick of the disease.

[4] "The Etiology of Yellow Fever: An Additional Note."
Jour. Amer. Med. Assoc., Feb. 16, 1901.

(3) An interval of about twelve days or more after contamination appears to be necessary before the mosquito is capable of conveying the disease.

(4) The bite of the mosquito at an earlier period after contamination does not appear to confer any immunity against a subsequent attack.

(5) Yellow fever can also be experimentally produced by the subcutaneous injection of blood taken from the general circulation during the first and second days of this disease.

(6) An attack of yellow fever, produced by the bite of the mosquito, confers immunity against the subsequent injection of the blood of an individual suffering from the non-experimental form of the disease.

(7) The period of incubation in thirteen cases of experimental yellow fever has varied from forty-one hours to five days and seventeen hours.

(8) Yellow fever is not conveyed by fomites, and hence disinfection of articles of clothing, bedding, or merchandise, supposedly contaminated by contact with those sick with this disease, is unnecessary.

(9) A house may be said to be infected with yellow fever only when there are present within its walls contaminated mosquitoes capable of conveying the parasite of this disease.

(10) The spread of yellow fever can be most effectually controlled by measures directed to the destruction of mosquitoes and the protection of the sick against the bites of these insects.

(11) While the mode of propagation of yellow fever has now been definitely determined, the specific cause of this disease remains to be discovered.

Dr. Reed's paper met with a most gratifying reception, which he describes in a letter to his wife, just before he sailed for home, as follows:

COLUMBIA BARRACKS,
QUEMADOS,
Feb. 6th, 1901.

To-day the paper was read and met with a most favourable reception. The attention during the reading was all that I could have asked for and the applause at its conclusion long and hearty. A resolution expressive of the high appreciation in which our work was held, together with the thanks of the Congress, was unanimously adopted. I received dozens of the warmest kind of handshakes from Cuban, Spanish, Mexican, South American, and North American physicians, men whom I had not even met. The hall was crowded and even the doors packed with listeners. It was indeed a signal triumph for our work.

When Dr. Reed returned early in February, Dr. Carroll remained behind in order to make some further observations upon the blood in yellow fever and also, especially, upon the urine. The following letter was written him by Dr. Reed during this interval:

SURGEON GENERAL'S OFFICE,
WASHINGTON, Feb. 26, 1901.

MY DEAR DOCTOR: I have yours of the 21st, and am afraid that this will not reach you before your departure. I want you to bring the reprints of our Prelimi-

nary Note, which I seem to have left behind uninten-
tionally. There were about a dozen of them. . . .

It is too bad that ———— would not take the bite
again, but I cannot blame him after ————'s experience. Still, 10 successes out of 13 attempts is a pretty
good record. We must present the clinical side of these
cases to the Association of American Physicians in May,
if possible. Neale is on the sick list, temporarily, with a
bad cold, and I am tied down to the Army Examining
Board. Weather still beastly, with no immediate hope
of a let-up. You made no mistake by remaining in Cuba
till March, as February has been simply atrocious.

Give my love to everybody and hurry back as fast
as you can. Welch, Osler, and Thayer are very enthu-
siastic over our work. Love to Agramonte when you
see him.   Sincerely yours,   REED.

The specific germ of yellow fever, however, had
not yet been found, and although its discovery was
not a matter of such vital importance as the mode
by which the disease is conveyed, there were some
points connected with it which the Commission
desired to investigate before they withdrew from
their labours.

Dr. Sternberg, who had always taken an intense
interest in the subject, made the following pro-
phetic suggestion concerning it, on page 531 of
his " Manual of Bacteriology," published in 1892:

The possibility, of course, remains that the specific
infectious agent in yellow fever may belong to an en-

tirely different class of micro-organisms from the bacteria, or that it may be ultra-microscopic, or not capable of demonstration in the tissues by the staining methods usually employed by bacteriologists.

In the early summer of 1901 Dr. William H. Welch, of the Johns Hopkins University, called Dr. Reed's attention to the experiments of Loeffler and Frosch, in which they had demonstrated that the specific infectious agent of foot and mouth disease in cattle would pass through a porcelain filter and was, therefore, too small to be discovered by the microscope. According to Loeffler and Frosch, there were two possible explanations of this result: either the filtered lymph held in solution an extraordinarily active toxin, or the specific agent of the disease was so minute as to pass through the pores of a filter which prevents the passage of the smallest bacteria. They themselves accepted the latter explanation, since they were able in later experiments by means of the filtered lymph to convey the disease through a series of six animals, the last of which sickened just as promptly after the injection of the filtered lymph as the first of the series. Having thus determined that the micro-organisms might be considered ultra-microscopic, Loeffler and Frosch offered the suggestion that, perhaps, the specific agent of some of the acute infectious diseases of man and the animals, such

as smallpox, scarlet fever, measles, rinderpest, etc.,
might belong to the same category. The remaining members of the Army Commission, Reed and
Carroll, considered that investigations carried out
along the lines just suggested might throw light
upon the ætiology of yellow fever, and as an outbreak of the disease at Santiago de las Vegas, near
Havana, in the summer of 1901 offered an opportunity of carrying on the necessary experiments,
Dr. Carroll returned to Cuba for the purpose,
landing at Havana on August 11, 1901. It was also
decided, at Dr. Carroll's suggestion, to test the
effect of moderate temperature upon the infectious
property of the serum.

Some months before Dr. Carroll's arrival an
inoculation station had been established in connection with Las Animas Hospital, under the charge
of Dr. John Guiteras, for the purpose of carrying
on inoculation experiments. These experiments
had been instituted, to use Dr. Guiteras' own
words, " not with a view *to control or confirm* the
conclusions of the United States Army Commission, for anyone who has followed their work with
unprejudiced attention must have concluded that
their solution of the problem of the ætiology of
yellow fever was final; but rather with the hope
of propagating the disease in a controllable form
and securing, among the recently arrived immi-

JAMES CARROLL, M.D.

Member of the U. S. A. Yellow Fever Commission. From a
photograph taken in 1901

grants, immunisation, with the minimum amount of danger." So far as immunisation was concerned, it may be said at once that the experiments did not fulfil the hopes which had been based upon them, the desired object, says Dr. Guiteras, " not being attainable by the present methods, without considerable risk to the individual."

Up to the time of Dr. Carroll's arrival in Havana, Dr. Guiteras had not succeeded in producing a single case of experimental yellow fever, a fact which was beginning to cause him and his colleagues some discouragement. Immediately after Dr. Carroll reached Las Animas Hospital, however, an experimental case did develop, and two days later Dr. Carroll wrote to Dr. Reed describing the situation as follows:

LAS ANIMAS HOSPITAL, HAVANA,
Aug. 13, 1901.

DEAR DOCTOR: I landed on Sunday morning after what would be called a very pleasant time as far as weather and sea were concerned, but I felt it all the same, and the company are several meals ahead.

Drs. Finlay, Guiteras, and Gorgas were very much put out over their failures, but now they are all very much elated. On the evening of my arrival the first case came down on the fourth day from four $3/19$ [5] insects

---

[5] This was a formula by which it was understood that the mosquitoes had bitten a yellow fever patient on the third day of the disease, and had been kept nineteen days before biting a well subject.

from a Santiago de las Vegas case. On the following day another man came down from similar insects from this case applied to both individuals at the same time.

I made a dozen 200 cc. bouillon flasks at Las Animas and am making preparations to draw blood from one of these individuals to-morrow. . . .

Everybody is very nice and I am hustling to get to work while the material is in sight. Guiteras has no more immunes in sight and some of his Spaniards have backed out. I shall telephone Colonel Havard to send me six subjects from Triscormia, and shall use three of them at once. In order to aid me in securing material with certainty, I have just asked for one thousand dollars. I spoke to Colonel Scott about it this morning and it will be all right. . . .

Our friends Bellazaghi and Caldos are located at Camp Lazear, waiting an opportunity to demonstrate the value of their specific serum. I learned from Colonel Havard yesterday that they claim to have the specific organism, and they inoculate horses with it so as to obtain the serum. They find it in black vomit and in the intestine and they produce yellow fever with it in dogs! Evidently colon or lactis aërogenes. The colonel says that they are willing to describe the characteristics of their organism, but they have bound themselves to some commercial concern, so that they cannot furnish a culture. I remarked that such methods of procedure were mercenary and unscientific, and if they believed they had the specific organism they were in duty bound to give it to the world, in order that their claims might be substantiated and they receive the credit due to them for such a valuable piece of work. A few drops under the skin of a few individuals would settle the point, and

I believe they know it, but the test would be too crucial for them. I have not had the pleasure of meeting them yet, and I am not wasting my time in seeking them.

Major Ross is exceedingly kind and asks to be remembered. As soon as I get any results I shall write to you again. With regards to all.

Very sincerely yours,

JAMES CARROLL.

Dr. Guiteras' satisfaction in his experimental cases was soon damped by the serious character that some of them assumed, and his anxiety manifested itself in extreme cautiousness as to permitting further experiments upon his patients, although Dr. Carroll had been sent to Cuba by the United States Government for that purpose and it was absolutely necessary to complete his final investigations that he should make them. Dr. Carroll's next letter to Dr. Reed describes his disappointment at the turn affairs were taking.

LAS ANIMAS HOSPITAL, HAVANA,

August 15, 1901.

MY DEAR DOCTOR: I have to record my first disappointment. When I last wrote you I was making preparations to draw blood from Dr. Guiteras' second case. It was a good one with a constant temperature of between 103° and 104° F., and I expected to draw blood from him yesterday. Early in the morning Dr. Guiteras advised against it, for the reason that the moral effect upon the man might be bad. He admitted that the man's general condition at the time was good, but he said that his promises to him did not include any such operation. The matter was decided by Major Ross, who has charge of the treatment of these cases and who, of course, sided with Guiteras. . . . You can imagine my disappointment. . . .

I have asked for three men to bite to-morrow with the same insects Dr. Guiteras used, for I must have some good cases. I expect to get Spaniards from Triscormia. I have also asked Colonel Havard for Ames or Amador to look after my patients while I am attending to my experiments. . . . With this arrangement there will be no quibbling about the drawing of a small quantity of blood from my own patients. I obtained half a dozen insects from Ames to-day, which his steward has been raising, and I shall apply them in the morning to the third case, at the end of the second day. . . .

I receive the fullest coöperation from General Scott. The allotment of $1,000 has been ordered and the per diem too. Mr. McCoy has also called to-day about my boxes, which have not arrived. I rely upon the Berkefeld filters and I have purchased hypodermic syringes here, so that I am equipped for work in the expectation of using these cases. I am not deterred, however, and shall go right ahead. . . .

I saw Drs. Bellazaghi and Caldos to-day. They have injected two Spaniards with their protective serum, and two others are to be used as controls when the biting is done. They will first administer another injection of what they call their vaccine. They say the immunity they confer lasts forty days. I learn this from Dr. Guiteras. . . .

With kind regards to everyone,
Very sincerely,
JAMES CARROLL.

Dr. Reed replied to these two letters as follows:

BLUE RIDGE SUMMIT, PA.,
Aug. 20, 1901.

MY DEAR CARROLL: Yesterday I received your first letter, and to-day your second came. I am intensely gratified to hear that Guiteras and Finlay have been able at last to confirm our experiments, although very sorry to learn that two of their cases are so severe. It was disappointing not to be permitted to draw blood from such a typical case, but you must know how timid —— is about anything like a surgical case. . . .

Sincerely yours,
WALTER REED.

A few days later Reed writes again:

BLUE RIDGE SUMMIT, PA.,
Aug. 23, 1901.

You were right in ignoring Caldos and Bellazaghi. Think of reputable physicians stooping to such unprofessional conduct! I am amazed that —— did not promptly inform the Surgeon General of the conduct of these men.

The disappointment about the Las Animas cases occasioned some delay in Dr. Carroll's observations, for he was obliged to produce cases of ex-

perimental yellow fever by inoculation of Spaniards who volunteered for pecuniary reasons, and
then draw blood for his further experiments from
these, instead of obtaining it without loss of time,
as he had expected to do, from Dr. Guiteras' cases.
I give a copy of the contract used between the
United States Government and the men who volunteered as subjects.

LAS ANIMAS HOSPITAL, HAVANA, CUBA,
Sept. 5, 1901.

I, Jeremiah Tomlinson, born in Lincoln, Neb., declare that I am twenty-five years of age, and that I
have no one dependent upon me for support.

Desiring to become immune to yellow fever, and fully
appreciating that in so doing I will probably contract
the disease, I hereby give my full and free consent to
the inoculation of my person through the bites of mosquitoes. In consideration of which I am to receive the
sum of seventy-five (75) dollars Am. Cy. if the inoculation fails, and two hundred (200) dollars if I contract
yellow fever as a result of said inoculation.

JEREMIAH TOMLINSON.

Witnesses { R. M. KIRBY SMITH,
CHARLES PARKER.

One of the difficulties encountered by Dr. Carroll at this time was associated with the terms of
this contract. The fact that a sum of money, no
matter how small, was paid to volunteers, whether
they contracted the disease or not, induced men

who had had yellow fever, and were, therefore, immune, to present themselves as subjects, and if no one but the man himself was in the secret he could do a little stroke of business without risk.

In spite of all these hindrances, Dr. Carroll set to work with his customary zeal and enthusiasm to secure conditions necessary to the prosecution of his researches; as soon as suitable cases of yellow fever were produced, his experiments were conducted along the following lines:

(1) Injection of the fresh blood taken from a vein at the bend of the elbow; (2) injection of unheated and partially defibrinated blood; (3) injection of partially defibrinated blood heated for ten minutes at $55°$ C.; (4) injection of diluted blood serum previously filtered through a Berkefeld laboratory filter.

The results of these experiments showed that of seven individuals who received subcutaneously the fresh or partially defibrinated blood in quantities of 0.5 to 5 cc., six (85.7 per cent.) developed an attack of yellow fever within the usual period of incubation of the disease, thus demonstrating that the specific agent of yellow fever is present in the blood, at least during the first, second, and third days of the attack, at which time the blood employed in the experiments was abstracted.

It also appeared that if, when blood had been

injected into the non-immune subject, additional blood was at once withdrawn in considerable quantity and transferred to tubes of nutritive bouillon, no organic growth could be obtained (except on one occasion *staphylococcus pyogenes citreus,* a skin-contaminating organism common in Cuba) even when a much smaller amount injected into the individual as a control sufficed to produce a severe attack of yellow fever.

It was further found that the specific agent contained in the blood was destroyed, or at any rate attenuated, by heating up to 55° C. for ten minutes, so that the injection of 1.5 cubic centimetres of the heated defibrinated blood was harmless, although the injection of 0.75 cubic centimetres of the same defibrinated blood, unheated, sufficed to induce a prompt attack of yellow fever in a control individual.

Of not less interest was the fact brought out by these experiments that yellow fever could be produced by the injection of a small quantity of bacteria—free filtrate, obtained by passing the diluted serum through a Berkefeld filter. The writers conclude with the following remarks: [6]

The production of yellow fever by the injection of blood serum that has previously been passed through

[6] " The Etiology of Yellow Fever: A Supplemental Note." Amer. Med., Feb. 22, 1902.

a filter capable of removing all test of bacteria is, we think, a matter of extreme importance and interest. The occurrence of the disease under such circumstances and within the usual period of incubation might be explained in one of two ways, viz., first, upon the supposition that the serum filtrate contains a toxin of considerable potency; or, second, that the specific agent of yellow fever is of such minute size as to pass readily through the pores of a Berkefeld filter.

In favour of the supposition that in yellow fever an active toxin is present in the blood, may be cited the early and marked jaundice; the free hæmorrhage from the mucous membrane of the mouth and stomach, doubtless due to profound changes in the capillary vessel-walls; the rapid progress of the disease to a fatal termination, the advanced fatty degeneration of the hepatic cells, as well as the marked parenchymatous changes found in the kidneys. If present in the blood, this toxin would in all likelihood be found in the serum filtrate obtained from the blood, and if injected in sufficient quantity might induce an attack of yellow fever in a susceptible individual after the usual period of incubation. In this respect it would bear analogy to the production of tetanus in the human being, after the usual period of incubation of this disease, by the subcutaneous injection of a very small quantity of tetanus toxin, as reported by Nicolas, in 1893, and more recently by Bolton, Fisch, and Walden.

Against the view that a toxin is present in the serum filtrate, we invite attention to the innocuousness of the partially defibrinated blood when heated to 55° C. for ten minutes. . . . Here the toxin, which must have been present in just the same quantity as in the serum filtrate obtained from this blood, appears to have been completely destroyed by the temperature above mentioned. Now, although certain bacteria are destroyed by this temperature, as yet we know of no bacteria toxin that is rendered inert by such a low degree of heat continued for such a short time. . . . The tetanus toxin which has been found to be the most sensitive thus far, requires, according to Kitasato,[7] a temperature of 60° C. for twenty minutes, or 55° C. for one and one half hours, in order to destroy its activity.

As a further test, and in order to determine whether the serum filtrate contained something more particulate than a soluble toxin, we availed ourselves of the opportunity of observing the effect that would follow the transference to a third individual of blood drawn from one of the patients whose attack had been occasioned by the injection of 1.5 cc. of serum filtrate. If under these circumstances it should be found that the injection of a small amount of blood was followed by an attack of yellow fever in a third individual, the evidence would point in the strongest manner to the presence of the disease in such blood, since we can hardly believe that a toxin which had undergone so great dilution in the body of the second individual would still be capable of producing the disease.

The patient who submitted to inoculation for the purpose of determining this crucial point was a young American non-immune, mentioned in the report simply as J. M. B. He was injected with

[7] The distinguished Japanese bacteriologist.

1.5 cc. of serum filtrate, and then, at the beginning of the eighth day after his first inoculation, was given a subcutaneous injection of 1.5 cc. of blood drawn from the venous circulation of a patient in whom the disease had followed the injection of 3 cc. of serum filtrate, representing 1.5 cc. of the undiluted serum. At the time of the inoculation the subject's condition was quite normal. After an inoculation of just twenty-four hours he developed a well-marked case of yellow fever, which ran a typical course and ended in prompt recovery. The incubation period of yellow fever in cases induced by the bite of the mosquito had been shown by Reed and by Guiteras to vary from six days one hour, in the longest case, to two days thirteen hours, in the shortest; while in cases produced by the injection of blood it varied from five days two hours to one day seventeen hours. " In view of this data," Reed and Carroll remark, " we believe that we are justified in expressing the opinion that the source of infection in the case just described must be attributed to the injection of blood rather than to the injection of filtered serum derived from the blood, and, further, that the blood contained the specific agent of yellow fever, which had, therefore, passed through the filter along with the filtrate with which the individual in this case had been inoculated."

During the experiments conducted by Dr. Carroll at this time an incident occurred which is an apt illustration of the disappointments and failures liable to overtake scientific investigators at all times, even though every source of disaster has, apparently, been guarded against. I give Dr. Carroll's account of it in full:

LAS ANIMAS HOSPITAL, HAVANA,
Sept. 24, 1901.

MY DEAR DOCTOR: I have a beautiful case now on hand, and if ——— had obeyed orders the serum test would have been made. It is a pronounced case, but appears to be doing well. . . .

Well, on Saturday morning I drove over to Santa Clara Battery, and arranged for my three men for this evening. From there I went to Quemados, drew more blood, made a few smears, examined fresh blood and urine, and applied mosquitoes. By 2 P. M. the serum had separated well (six hours), and was transferred with a pipette to a test-tube, both being sterile. After dinner at Las Animas I proceeded to the laboratory to filter it. My pump had been tested and found to work perfectly, and ——— was directed to place it under lock and key and not to allow any person to interfere with it. A closet of large size was available, and only he and I had keys to it.

It was already dark and I was working by gaslight, and as I had promised to come for the men at 7 P. M. I had no time to lose in order to inject the filtrate that night. I took it for granted that the pump had not been disturbed, but after the first few strokes the filter was forced out of the flask (—— was holding both) with considerable force, fell on the table, and was broken, losing all the serum! The valve attachment of the pump had been reversed, so that a positive instead of a negative pressure was obtained, with the result stated. The valve attachment was easily reversible, but I had made it a point never to change it since I saw it work in the store in New York. —— had evidently unscrewed the thing, and replaced it in the same position, as he thought. There was nothing on the outside to indicate the position of the pump valve, which he thought was in the plunger of the pump. Instead, it is screwed in as a separate piece between the nozzle and the barrel. As the heavy pressure tubing remained tied to the nozzle, there was no reason to suppose it had been disturbed, but I did notice that instead of taking the pump from the closet that was locked, he took it from the adjoining one, which was not locked. This leads me to believe that in his confidence in his mechanical ability he had taken the thing apart to show some one, and had neglected to return it to its proper compartment.

I had tested the outfit a number of times, and it had never failed to work perfectly, generating a tremendous pressure. —— denies absolutely any knowledge of manipulation, but subsequent events prove him to be a ready liar. I had directed him a number of times to say nothing to any person about the work, or anything connected with it. This morning I met Dr. Guiteras, and told him I had a case at last. He replied: " Yes, so I hear. It was too bad that you had an accident with your serum. —— says that there was too much vaseline on the plunger, and it clogged the valve! " —— denied having spoken a word, but I convinced him that I knew better, and advised him if he valued his job to keep his mouth closed. I have been keeping as dumb as an oyster while he has been keeping people posted on my work!

To this letter Reed replied: " I should have been tempted to have dynamited —— had I been there. It only goes to show that you cannot trust *anybody!* "

With these experiments of Dr. Carroll's at Las Animas the business of the Army Commission came to an end, and Dr. Reed's own active work in yellow fever ceased, although his interest in the subject continued unchanged during the remainder of his life. The results obtained by Dr. Carroll were embodied by the Commission in a paper presented to the Society of American Bacteriologists when it met at Chicago at the close of the year 1901, which was published in American Medicine for February 22, 1902, under the title, " The Etiology of Yellow Fever: A Supplemental Note." This was the last publication issued in the name of the Commission, but some other interesting papers on the subject were published later by Dr. Carroll, and will be discussed elsewhere.

Before concluding this chapter, a word must be said concerning the debt which the world owes to Major-General Leonard Wood, the Military Governor of Cuba, for his active and intelligent interest in the work of the Army Commission. When application was made to General Wood for permission to conduct experiments on non-immune persons, together with a request for a liberal supply of money to be expended in rewarding volunteers who should submit themselves to experiment, both money and authority were liberally granted. It was most fortunate for the work that General Wood was not only a man of sound judgment and extended sympathies, but that his scientific training enabled him to comprehend the nature of the experiments which Dr. Reed proposed to undertake, and to appreciate their value to the world at large.

Dr. Reed, in making acknowledgment of General Wood's kindness, says: "Without his approval and assistance these observations could not have been carried out." But, even more than this: had the head of affairs in Cuba been a man of less intelligence, less breadth, or less knowledge, the work might, and probably would, have been far less fruitful of benefit to humanity. Wherever the recent discoveries concerning yellow fever are known, and protective measures based upon them are employed for the safety of communities, General Wood's hearty support of Major Reed and his colleagues should be remembered with respect and gratitude.

CHAPTER VIII

PRACTICAL APPLICATION OF THE MOSQUITO THEORY OF YELLOW FEVER

Disease and her ravening offspring, Pain with the thousand teeth,
He drave into night primeval, the nethermost worlds beneath.
——WILLIAM WATSON, *The Dream of Man.*

LET us now consider for a moment the practical results of Dr. Reed's discovery; in other words, let us ascertain whether a town or district can actually be freed from yellow fever, or protected against its invasion, by the use of methods based on the theory of mosquito inoculation. And, if so, what are these methods in detail?

The best answer to the first of these questions will be found in Dr. Reed's own account of the results of his theory when put into practice in the city of Havana, published in the Journal of Hygiene for April, 1902:

The importance of the discovery that yellow fever is transmitted by the bite of a certain species of mosquito did not fail to attract the prompt attention of the military governor of Cuba, himself a physician, and formerly a distinguished member of the Medical Department of the United States Army. By his direction the theory was subjected to a practical test in the city of Havana, in which city yellow fever had not failed to make its yearly appearance during the past one hundred and forty years.

Under the efficient management of the chief officer, Surgeon-Major William Gorgas, U. S. A., the sanitary regulations were so far modified as to require that every patient having yellow fever should not only be quarantined, but that his room should be promptly protected with wire screens, so as to prevent the possibility of mosquitoes becoming infected by sucking the blood of the patient. As a second important measure, a systematic destruction of all mosquitoes in other rooms of the patient's house, as well as in adjoining houses, was at once begun, the fumes of pyrethrum being relied upon to stupefy the insects, after which they were carefully swept up and buried. In other words, Surgeon-Major Gorgas, relying upon the well-known slow progress of yellow-fever, sought to destroy all mosquitoes, infected or non-infected, within a given radius of each case, while at the same time he effectually excluded all mosquitoes from access to the sick. If a secondary case occurred, the same hygienic measures were vigorously enforced along the lines indicated.

As an illustration of what has been accomplished by these newer sanitary regulations, I may say that, counting from the date when they were put into force, *viz.*, February 15, 1901, Havana was freed from yellow fever within ninety days; so that from May 7 to July 1, a period of fifty-four days, no cases occurred. Notwithstanding the fact that on the latter date and during the months of July, August, and September, the disease was repeatedly reintroduced into Havana from an inland town, no difficulty was encountered in promptly stamping it out by the same measures of sanitation, intelligently applied, both in the city of Havana and in the town of Santiago de las Vegas, whence the disease was being brought into Havana.

As a further illustration of the remarkable sanitary victory accomplished over a disease whose progress we have heretofore been powerless to arrest, I will close this paper by inviting the reader's attention first to the accompanying Chart I., which shows the average mortality from yellow fever in Havana for the twenty years 1880-1899, inclusive, and also the mortality by month for the years 1900 and 1901. I will then ask him to examine Chart II., which shows the progress of yellow fever in Havana during the epidemic year ending March 1, 1901, when the sanitary authorities were putting forth every effort known at the time to sanitary science in order to control the march of the disease, and when he has satisfied himself that no effect whatever was produced upon the epidemic of that year, I will invite his attention to Chart III., which shows the occurrence of that disease in Havana for the epidemic year March 1, 1901, to March 1, 1902, during which year yellow fever was fought on the theory that the specific agent of this disease is transmitted solely by means of the bites of infected mosquitoes. By carefully comparing the figures both as to deaths and cases in these two charts, and recalling that between the years 1853 and 1900 there have been recorded in the city of Havana 35,952 deaths from yel-

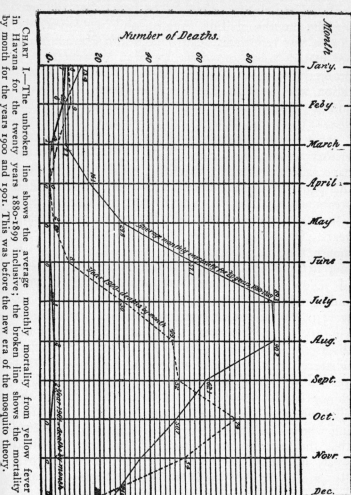

CHART I.—The unbroken line shows the average monthly mortality from yellow fever in Havana for the twenty years 1880-1899 inclusive; the broken line shows the mortality by month for the years 1900 and 1901. This was before the new era of the mosquito theory.

low fever, he will then be able to more clearly appreciate the value of the work accomplished by the American Army Commission.

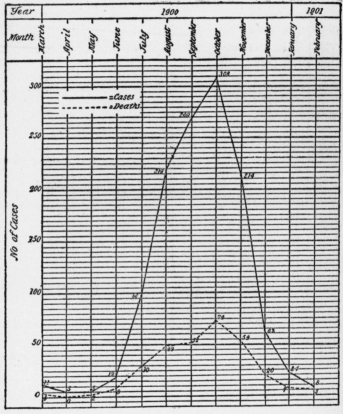

CHART II.—Shows the progress of yellow fever in Havana during the epidemic year ending March 1, 1901, when the Sanitary authorities were putting forth every effort known to sanitary science in order to control the disease. The unbroken line shows the number of cases, while the broken line gives the mortality. This also was in the pre-mosquito period.

To this statement Major J. R. Kean, who used the paper in a somewhat abridged form after Dr. Reed's death, adds the following footnote:

Not a single case of yellow fever occurred in Havana during the year 1902, nor, so far as known, in the Island of Cuba.—J. R. K.

These facts speak for themselves, but a more detailed demonstration of the practical value of

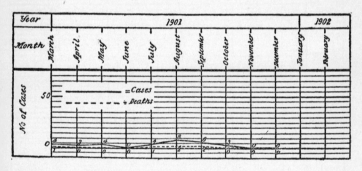

CHART III.—Shows the occurrence of yellow fever in Havana for the epidemic year March 1, 1901, to March 1, 1902, during which year yellow fever was fought on the theory that the specific agent of the disease is transmitted by means of infected mosquitoes. Note the extraordinary contrast between Chart III, under the new régime, and Charts I and II, under the old.

Dr. Reed's theory is given in the results obtained by Dr. G. M. Guiteras, in 1903, at Laredo, Texas. Dr. Guiteras's work also affords an interesting insight into the details of the method by which disinfection based on the mosquito theory is carried out, and shows that the desired end can be attained under adverse conditions, such as were present in Laredo, as well as under the favourable circumstances which obtained in Havana.

In 1903 Dr. Guiteras was appointed by the Surgeon-General to investigate the epidemic at Laredo, a town of 18,000 inhabitants, and he arrived there on September 25, 1903, in company with Dr. George R. Tabor, State health officer of Texas. On their arrival they found that yellow fever had already obtained a firm foothold and was widely disseminated in a population consisting almost entirely of non-immunes; it was also firmly established in the little neighbouring town of Nuevo Laredo, containing about 8000 inhabitants, and separated from Laredo itself by the River Rio Grande, over which there are various avenues of communication. There was reason to believe that the disease had been imported directly from Monterey, having originally come from Tampico, Mexico, along the line of the Mexican National Railroad.

On investigation it was found that the *stegomyia fasciata* was present in enormous quantities and widely distributed, the conditions of the water supply being such as to afford every facility for its active propagation. A private water-works company supplied both towns, but as its rates were too high for the poorer classes, the latter were in the habit of buying water from carts driven along the streets, which obtained their supply directly from the river. The water from both sources was so muddy that it was the universal custom to use barrels as receptacles, for the purpose of allowing the water to settle. Every house was supplied with from one to ten of these water-casks, which, as a matter of course, were kept in sheds or dark and shady corners. As Dr. Guiteras says, it would be difficult to improve on them as breeding places for mosquitoes. The houses of the poorer classes were of the worst type, many of them being simply adobe huts with thatched roofs, which consist of one room, and possibly a shed at the back, used for a kitchen. Others are made of lumber, with no attempt at apposition between the planks, and others again are partly or wholly constructed of tin or of iron, with just enough lumber to attach these thereto.

On the 26th of September [says Dr. Guiteras],[1] an office was established in the central part of the city for the transaction of business and on the following day the sanitary corps under my command was given a definite organisation. Four mosquito sections had been formed, with an acting assistant surgeon in charge of each,

[1] "The Yellow Fever Epidemic of 1903, at Laredo, Texas." Jour. Amer. Med. Assoc., July 9, 1904.

and Past Assistant-Surgeon Von Ezdorf given general supervision over the entire squad. Each section consisted of about eight men, one of whom was a carpenter, and another was designated as foreman and had charge of the material. Each section was supplied with a cart containing all the material necessary for the work, to wit: Sulphur and pyrethrum powder in sufficient quantity, twenty-five pots, twenty-five pans, five-gallon can of wood alcohol, roll of paper, shears, knives, bucket of paste, brushes, brooms, wall-brushes, mosquito netting, a number of strips of lath, nails, hatchet, saw, ready-made screen doors and windows, ladder, five-gallon can of kerosene oil.

Within a short time the above system was somewhat modified, with the object of gaining time and effectiveness. The carpenters were separated from the general disinfecting section and formed at first into two and later into three " screening " sections. These were composed each of two or three carpenters, supplied with a wagon carrying tools, lumber, mosquito bars, and mosquito netting. The *modus operandi* was then as follows:

Immediately on a case (whether suspicious or positive) being reported to us by the state board of health or by anyone having authority to do so, a screening section was at once sent out and the infected house " screened." This " screening " varied according to circumstances. Unnecessary doors and windows were shut tight. One window and a door of the patient's room were left open for ventilation and to admit those caring for him, and both of these were fitted with wire screens. Often the conditions did not admit of this. The shacks or " jacals " of the poorer classes consisted of but one room

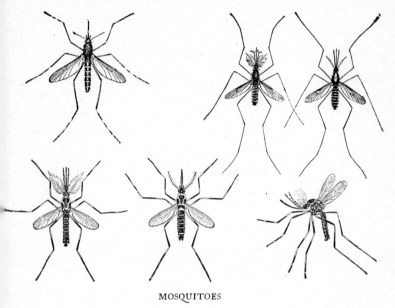

MOSQUITOES

The lower left-hand figure is the adult male yellow fever mosquito.

The middle lower figure is the adult female yellow fever mosquito, by means of which the disease is transmitted.

The lower right-hand figure shows the male yellow fever mosquito, from the side.

The two upper right-hand figures are the male and female (male to the left) the *Anopheles maculipennis*—the malarial mosquito.

The left-hand upper figure shows the *Culex sollicitans*, the common Atlantic coast ring-legged mosquito.

These figures are used by the courtesy of L. O. Howard, Ph.D.

with innumerable openings in the walls and rooms. Screening was impracticable here, and the patient was placed under a mosquito bar. Towards the end of the epidemic I had a portable mosquito house built, covered with wire gauze and with double doors, which was applicable to such cases. The patient being thus isolated and rendered as safe as possible against propagating the disease by infecting the mosquito, the disinfecting section would come along and disinfect the premises and surrounding houses to kill the insects already infected. It was also the duty of the disinfecting section to pour oil into all cisterns, barrels, or other receptacles of stagnant waters found on the premises disinfected.

The details of the disinfecting process were as follows: The room or house was made mosquito-tight. To accomplish this, all doors and windows were closed. Paper was then cut into strips and pasted over all cracks or openings through which mosquitoes might escape; the chimney was made secure. In many cases houses were in such bad condition that they had to be almost completely papered over, both inside and out, and large unprotected openings covered entirely with sheets of paper. In the meantime the pots were being filled with sulphur or pyrethrum, as the case might demand, and placed in position on pans filled with water. These water-pans served a double purpose, to prevent danger from fire and for the purpose of collecting mosquitoes, for experience had shown that after disinfection nearly all the dead mosquitoes within the room were found in the pans. . . .

The pots and pans being in position, about fifty cubic centimetres of alcohol were poured on the sulphur, or pyrethrum, as the case might be, and the contents ignited. Then, without loss of time, the disinfectors would retire, closing the last door of exit and pasting paper over any cracks that might be found in it. When the house admitted of it, all rooms except that of the patient were first disinfected, and he was then removed to one of the disinfected rooms, duly protected from mosquitoes, so as to permit of the disinfection of the room occupied by him. . . . For the purpose of mosquito disinfection, sulphur was burned in the proportion of four pounds to the one thousand cubic feet, with four hours' exposure; pyrethrum, six pounds to the one thousand cubic feet, with six hours' exposure. On the termination of the disinfection the house was opened and the floors, walls, furniture, etc., carefully swept for the purpose of collecting all asphyxiated mosquitoes and immediately incinerating them. . . .

The above plan was adhered to until the end of the epidemic, with the modification that the duties of oiling cisterns, barrels, and receptacles of all kinds assumed such proportions that on October 9 an oiling section was organised and set to work. This section was put in charge of Acting Assistant-Surgeon Frick, with a wagon carrying the necessary material. Subsequently it was divided into two sections, one attending to the sprinkling of the streets, pools, ponds, and other large bodies of standing water; the other looking after water-barrels, cisterns, pails, tin cans, and all other water containers found in the neighbourhood of houses.

Naturally much opposition arose against the oiling of the water-barrels, especially among the ignorant classes, who were led to believe that our object was to poison the water. On several occasions this opposition assumed serious and menacing proportions, so much so that the lives of the officers and men engaged in the work were threatened. To obviate this difficulty it was decided to put wooden faucets into the barrels of drinking water, so that the water might be drawn from below, free from oil contamination. The oiling section was duly supplied with these faucets, with instructions to apply them to all barrels containing water for drinking purposes. This measure was very effective in allaying irritation and avoiding trouble with the people. . . . Within a short time the oiling section, under its efficient chief, became so apt in its duties that the entire city could be inspected and oiled in five or six days, so that within that time every water container and other deposit of standing water was inspected and treated, making it impossible for the mosquito larvæ to arrive at maturity.

In spite of all these efforts the epidemic continued to increase so alarmingly that disinfection of infected houses was not found sufficient, and a systematic and complete disinfection of the entire city was begun. Two sections of disinfecting parties were started, therefore, one at the southeast and another at the northeast extremities of the town, working towards each other. Every house and building was included in this disinfection: schools, public buildings, and churches, no matter whether they had or had not been previously disinfected. The following table, published by Dr. Guiteras, gives an estimate of the work done from September 26 to November 30:

Houses or rooms screened..........   304
Patients screened under mosquito bars.   115
Houses disinfected   2,952
Rooms disinfected 10,045

It was estimated on careful calculation that there were at that time 2963 houses in Laredo, and of these 580, or 19.54 per cent., were infected.

Great difficulty was experienced in carrying out the work on account, especially, of the lack of authority to enforce the necessary procedures and the ignorant prejudice of the people. A large part of the inhabitants of Laredo were possessed of the idea that the physicians and the authorities were in a conspiracy to make money. They even went so far as to believe very generally that the physicians poisoned their patients to get rid of them and thus end the epidemic, and, incredible as it may appear, these opinions were supported by one or two (irresponsible) newspapers published in Laredo. Under these circumstances it is not surprising that all possible means were used to secrete cases of yellow fever from the physicians and inspectors. Patients very ill with the disease would hide themselves or be hidden by their relatives, until at last it became necessary to institute a house-to-house inspection under the direction of the health officer, and, later, of volunteer inspectors, appointed by the Mayor. After a short time these efforts were supplemented by the better class of citizens, who became interested in the work and offered their services.

Lack of authority to carry out sanitary measures was, however, the most important obstacle to success, and it may be said here, once and for all, that the course of affairs in Laredo showed that results such as were obtained in Havana during the American occupation cannot be achieved, if the disease is at all widespread, unless undisputed authority is placed in the hands of the sanitary authorities by Government. The power exercised in Havana really amounted to martial law, and when it is considered what the shortening of an epidemic means in the saving of life, the reducing of expenditure, and the conservation of commercial and railroad interests, it becomes, as Dr. Guiteras says:

A serious question whether under such circumstances the establishment of martial law, or something equivalent to it, should not be the first step taken in the suppression of an outbreak of yellow fever, or, in fact, any of the epidemic diseases. . . . In most epidemics the hardships endured by the people, the loss of life, the interruption of commerce, causing heavy financial losses, all are greater than in the case of riots or other financial disturbances of the peace for which ordinarily martial law is imposed. Such being the case, it is not clear why this efficient means of combating an epidemic should not be more strongly recommended, nor why so much opposition should be aroused against it when it is suggested.

Under martial law the Laredo epidemic could have been controlled, in Dr. Guiteras's opinion, within three or four weeks after the disease had been officially declared, on September 25, while, as a matter of fact, the desired end was not attained for nearly two months, the quarantine against Laredo by the State of Texas not being raised until November 30. Even under all disadvantages, however, the disease was completely eradicated.

Further conclusive evidence of the practical value of Dr. Reed's discovery has been given to the world since this memoir of him was begun, by the records of the epidemic in New Orleans in 1905.

I have been so fortunate as to obtain, through the good offices of my friend, Dr. Rudolph Matas, a brief account of this epidemic from the pen of Dr. J. H. White, Surgeon of the United States Public Health and Marine Hospital Service, who was in command at New Orleans during the summer of 1905:

NEW ORLEANS, LA.,
November 21, 1905.

DR. RUDOLPH MATAS,
MY DEAR DOCTOR MATAS: In compliance with your request, I submit the following statement with regard

to the yellow fever epidemic of 1905, and am sorry that all the statements made cannot be exact, for the reason that the data have not as yet been worked up.

From information at hand, it appears that the local Board of Health, being informed on the 12th day of July of the existence of yellow fever in the neighbourhood of the French Market, undertook to stamp it out by the fumigation of infected houses, the emptying of water barrels, and the oiling of cisterns, etc., in accordance with modern ideas, but with untrained men and means entirely inadequate for the huge task which confronted them, it being probable that Dr. Kohnke's estimate of 100 cases and 20 deaths up to July 20, was an under-, rather than an over-, estimate, and the number of concealed foci, therefore, in excess of what he had supposed.

For two or three years prior to this time Dr. Kohnke, as City Health Officer, had endeavoured to inculcate the idea of mosquito transmission, and, although his efforts were apparently unsuccessful, there must have been some results accomplished, as shown by the readiness with which all classes of the people subscribed to this doctrine in July and August, there being practically no exception worthy of mention, outside of the superstitious and ignorant alien population.

The Citizens Volunteer Ward Organisation, under the command of the Rev. Dr. Beverley Warner, began on or about July 24 a general fight on the mosquito, which was of great value, as may be readily seen, it being beyond question that a great reduction in the number of mosquitoes took place as a result thereof, the number to be infected being necessarily reduced in like proportion.

It is difficult to estimate how many cases existed on the 21st day of July, when the presence of the epidemic became known to the world at large, my own estimate being 148 cases and 24 deaths as the minimum, and a mathematical calculation would lead back to about the middle of May, possibly earlier, as the date of the first case.

On the 4th of August the citizens requested that the work of eliminating the disease be turned over to the Public Health and Marine Hospital Service, sending a message to this effect to the President, and the necessary orders were issued.

The funds for all of the work, except the pay of the officers, were furnished by the citizens, the State, and the city; on August 8 the work was placed in charge of the Public Health and Marine Hospital Service, and on the next day organisation was begun. I wish to make it plain that there was one central organisation prior to the time the Service took control, and that the division of the work and *establishment of ward organisations was made by me* because I believed the work too stupendous to be handled from one office. Seventeen sub-headquarters were therefore established.

When the Service took hold of the work there had been 616 cases and 112 deaths by the record, and four days after this the maximum daily report was made, showing 105 cases on August 12. After this the number of cases per day declined, until the date in September shortly following drastic measures taken to ascertain concealed cases, which action was followed by a sharp rise in the number of cases, which, in turn, was succeeded by a genuine decline that continued to the end.

As previously stated, there was practically no opposition to the sanitary measures after the starting of the campaign of education by the medical profession and the Citizens Volunteer Ward Organisation, and it may be stated, broadly, that within one week there was no opposition worthy to be called such.

I had never before had the pleasure of seeing a cosmopolitan population, or even one of a homogenous character, respond so readily to rational teaching and place so little obstruction in the way of the rational work which was necessary to be done. The gigantic natural difficulties in the way, the topography of the city lending itself to the breeding of mosquitoes, made the co-operation of the profession and of the people at large an absolutely essential pre-requisite to success, which co-operation, I am glad to say, was freely given and success attained.

The work itself was done from the ward headquarters, seventeen in number, of which I have spoken above, and was performed entirely in accordance with the findings of Walter Reed, the first step in any case of known infection being to thoroughly screen the sick room and place a mosquito bar over the patient, following this as soon thereafter as possible with a total destruction of all mosquitoes, both in the sick room and in the house. All rooms were sealed with paper strips on the inside, in order to prevent the mosquitoes from getting into cracks and thus escaping the fumigation. In every reported case, where opportunity was offered, an effort was made to trace its origin; namely, to ascertain at what house the patient had visited during the six days preceding his illness, and in this way many hitherto unknown foci were discovered and blotted out.

To give some idea of the vastness of such an undertaking in a city having a population of 325,000, with infection scattered from one end to the other, the following facts should be borne in mind.

The total area of this city occupied by dwellings and places of business is 44 square miles, although the geographical area is 196 square miles. There are, approximately, 60,000 houses and 70,000 cisterns.

During this period of our work we used a sufficient quantity of a five to ten per cent. solution of salt to salt 75 miles of gutters, this requiring nearly 3,000,000 pounds of rock salt.

We made 300,000 house-to-house inspections; disinfected 55,151 rooms, burning for this purpose, in round figures, 200 tons of sulphur and 5000 pounds of pyrethrum. We used about 60,000 gallons of oil in gutters and cisterns.

There were employed in the work 25 commissioned officers, 42 acting assistant surgeons, and three pharmacists, while the number of disinfectors, screeners, and ordinary labourers employed from time to time was over 4000, the largest number at any one time being 1276.

The cost of the campaign to the Public Health and Marine Hospital Service was about $50,000; and to the city, including the sums appropriated by the State, the city, and the citizens, $240,000, making a grand total of about $290,000.

The last well-authenticated case of yellow fever was reported on the 5th day of November, and of cases which obtained their infection in the city there have been practically none since the 1st of November.

At the present writing, November 21, there has been no frost nor any very near approach thereto.

I wish to accentuate the fact that, accepting Reed's findings *in toto,* and not in part, I did not quarantine against infected communities, but allowed people from such places to enter the city freely, simply watching them in order that any developing case might be cared for. This involved a little trouble and expense, but no harm was done, and the additional expense thus incurred was not a tithe of what would have been necessary in an effort to quarantine the city. I cannot too strongly express my views on this point, and one of the prime objects I had in view from first to last was to illustrate to the people of New Orleans and to the world at large, that under rational methods there is no more necessity for quarantining a city against yellow fever than there would be to do so against typhoid fever. If the people and the profession will co-operate, there is absolutely no danger of a spread, and I believe it a duty incumbent upon the latter to preach this doctrine until it is universally accepted. It certainly was demonstrated here by allowing several hundred people to come into New Orleans from Patterson and other infected points, and to go freely wherever they would in the city, no harm resulting in any instance.   Very sincerely yours,

J. H. WHITE.

A strong proof of the assurance of safety afforded by the present methods of fighting yellow fever and of the confidence arising from them is shown by the cheerful spirit with which the citizens of New Orleans encountered the epidemic of 1905, and the light-heartedness which pervaded the town, in marked contrast to the gloom that, in former times, always hung like a pall over such scenes. Mr. Rupert Boyce, Dean of the Liverpool School of Tropical Diseases, who was sent to New Orleans by that association as envoy charged to investigate yellow fever, has described this state of things most graphically in the Southern Magazine for October, 1905.

In one respect New Orleans has set an example to all the world in the fight against yellow fever. Coming, as I did, a stranger, but a stranger who has seen many campaigns against similar diseases, the first impression that struck me was the complete organisation of the citizens, and the rational and reasonable way in which the fight has been conducted by them. When I alighted from the car the first thing that greeted my eyes was a placard—of which tens of thousands have been distributed—bearing the words:

WEAR A SMILE ON YOUR FACE
AND A
FLOWER IN YOUR BUTTONHOLE.

Everywhere I went I saw these. The force with which such evidences of the light-hearted spirit in which the citizens of New Orleans sallied forth to win this fight strikes one who has been a witness to the profound gloom, distress, and woe that cloud every other epidemic city cannot be estimated.

That is the spirit which has led to victory. That is the light heart and gay song which nerves the warrior to invincibility. To go at the enemy laughing, and to fight with a jest, means always to overcome with a glorious victory.

When I came, in the first part of September, I found the whole country organised. The municipality was organised by wards; the medical profession was organised by flying squadrons; the State was organised by parishes. With a tangible enemy in view, the army of defence could begin to fight rationally and scientifically. Every individual citizen of every city and town, but especially of New Orleans, had taken to himself new heart of grace, because he knew what he had to fight.

To me, coming as I did from many campaigns against tropical diseases in many an odd corner of the world, this organisation appealed more strongly than I can say. An example to the world has been set, an example to every city in the civilised world which shall henceforth be attacked by similar diseases.

And the work of the Marine Hospital Service struck the heart of the beholder with joy. Cleanly, swiftly, scientifically, the olive-green uniforms darted hither and thither, into dens of filth and obscurity, opening up every corner to the bright light of science, working heroically, and withal so swiftly that it was like watching a huge machine, well oiled and efficacious, performing a marvellous task with perfect show of ease.

I subjoin a table, furnished me by Dr. L. O. Howard, of the United States Department of Agriculture, showing figures comparing the recent epidemic at New Orleans with those of previous years. The table was drawn up for epidemics prior to 1905 by Dr. Stanford E. Chaillé, the figures for 1905 having been added by Dr. White or one of his assistants. The epidemics of 1867 and 1878 are those which should be compared with those of 1905, and on doing so it will be seen that whereas there were 3107 deaths in 1867 and 4046 in 1878, there were only 452 in 1905, although the epidemic of the latter year promised in the beginning to be more severe than the others. It should also be noted that the Public Health and Marine Hospital Service did not begin its anti-mosquito work until August 12, of 1905. It is, as Dr. Howard says, an overwhelming proof of the efficacy of treatment on the mosquito basis.

COMPARATIVE TABLE OF DEATHS FROM YELLOW
FEVER IN NEW ORLEANS

MONTHS	1847	1848	1853	1854	1855	1858	1867	1878	1905
May...............			2						
June...............		4	31	2	5	2	3		
July...............	74	33	1521	29	382	132	11	26	57
August............	965	200	5133	532	1286	1140	255	1025	224
September..........	1100	467	982	1234	874	2204	1637	1780	111
October	198	126	147	490	97	1137	1072	1065	56
November	12	20	28	131	19	224	103	147	4
December..........	10		4	7	7	15	26	3	
Months unknown....	445	22							
Totals...........	2804	872	7848	2425	2670	4854	3107	4046	452

The epidemics of 1848, 1854, and 1855 are least comparable for 1905, because they immediately succeeded severe epidemics to which were due very many immunes.

Population of New Orleans by U. S. Census, 130,565 in 1850; 168,675 in 1860; 191,418 in 1870; 216,090 in 1880; and 287,104 in 1900.

Dr. White, it will be noticed, speaks strongly against unnecessary quarantine regulations, believing that the struggle with yellow fever on Dr. Reed's principles renders such regulations as prevailed in former times entirely superfluous, while the injury they inflict on commercial interests can hardly be estimated. I think that before leaving this subject some account of Dr. Reed's own views on the subject of quarantine will be in place.[2]

Under the admirable system of inspection and reports as carried out by the Marine Hospital Service, the appearance of yellow fever at any foreign port is promptly reported for the information of the health authorities of our several Atlantic ports. We may therefore, divide foreign ports within the so-called epidemic zone into (1) infected and (2) non-infected ports. Heretofore no distinction has been made by the health officers of our Southern ports as regards quarantine regulations from April 1 to November 1 between infected and non-infected places. All ports within the

[2] "The Prevention of Yellow Fever." Med. Rec., Oct. 26, 1901.

epidemic zone of yellow fever were considered as being infected places, and hence passengers and vessels were subjected to disinfection of both baggage and cargoes.

With our present knowledge of the way in which yellow fever is propagated, we believe that in the treatment of passengers, as well as of cargoes, a sharp distinction should be made, first, between infected and non-infected ports, and second, in the case of vessels sailing from infected ports, between those that have received their cargoes and passengers in mid-stream and those that have loaded at the wharf. We believe that no quarantine restrictions should be placed upon either passengers or cargo from non-infected ports. In the case of a vessel loading in mid-stream at an infected port by means of lighters, we believe that she can only receive infection in one way, *i. e.*, by passengers who have been exposed to yellow fever on shore, and who, coming on board, may thereafter be seized with the disease. The possibility of infected mosquitoes reaching the vessel either by flight or by means of lighters, may be considered as highly improbable.

Vessels loaded under the foregoing circumstances, *i. e.*, by lighters in mid-stream, and arriving at our ports without yellow fever developed *en route* should have their non-immune passengers quarantined for five days, counting the time consumed by the voyage as part of the quarantine period, and should be allowed to discharge their cargoes without delay. If the disease has developed *en route* among the crew or passengers, the sick should be promptly removed—the forecastle or staterooms, as the case may be, thoroughly disinfected with sulphur or formaldehyde gas, and the vessel allowed to proceed to her wharf.

On the other hand, if the vessel has received her cargo at the wharf of an infected port, there is a possibility that she may have received infection in one of three ways: first, either by contaminated mosquitoes that have bitten a case of yellow fever in the immediate vicinity on shore; second, by mosquitoes that have become infected from biting a yellow fever patient present on another vessel loading at the same, or an adjacent wharf; or, third, by some individual who has acquired an infection on shore and afterward taken passage on the vessel.

In our opinion, however, the chances of infection of a vessel from contaminated mosquitoes coming aboard from a house or ship in close proximity are very slight, although such a possibility must be admitted, as well as the further possibility that recently infected mosquitoes may have sought refuge on the vessel during the night preceding her departure. It is also possible that a case of mild, and hence undetected, yellow fever, may occur on board, and be the source for the infection of mosquitoes already present in the vessel.

Under these circumstances, if a sufficient number of days have not elapsed between her port of departure and her port of arrival in the United States, *i. e.,* sixteen to twenty-one days, to demonstrate the presence of the infected mosquitoes by the occurrence of a case or cases of yellow fever *en route,* we know of no way of absolutely excluding the possibility of importation of the disease by such a vessel, than by detention of all non-immune passengers for such number of days as will show their freedom from infection, and by careful disinfection of crew's and passengers' quarters. If more than twenty days have elapsed during the voyage without the occurrence of yellow fever, we see no good reason why either passengers or vessel should be detained.

We have said nothing about the disinfection of the vessel's cargo for the reason that we do not consider this to be necessary. The only possible excuse for subjecting the cargo to disinfection would be the fear of the presence of infected mosquitoes in the vessel's hold, provided she had loaded at the wharf of an infected port. In this instance, if the voyage has consumed five or more days, all mosquitoes contained in the hold will have died; for, *stegomyia fasciata* lives only two days if deprived of water. We cannot too strongly insist that the danger of importation of yellow fever into the United States lies, not in the cargo or personal baggage, but in the individual sick with the disease. With our present knowledge of its propagation, personal baggage should no longer be subjected to disinfection, and with our increased ability to prevent its spread by measures easy of application, instances should be few and exceptional when a vessel coming from a yellow fever port should be delayed longer than will be necessary to remove her non-immune passengers who have not completed their period of five days since leaving the port of departure.

The chief duty of quarantine officers hereafter will consist in the detection of mild, or very mild, cases of yellow fever. . . . While the exclusion of such cases is of the greatest importance, we doubt, however, whether, with our improved knowledge of how to prevent the spread of yellow fever, it would be advisable to place a greater burden upon ship's passengers by extending the quarantine period to more than five days. It appears to us rather, that, in view of the troublesome delays to which passengers and vessels from yellow fever ports have been subjected in the past, the time has now arrived, when standing upon more solid ground, we will be justified in seeking in every way to lessen as much as possible the restrictions placed by present quarantine regulations upon the ship's cargo, while we are adding to those of the passengers.

Anyone who reads the little volume of quarantine regulations issued in 1899 by Surgeon-General Walter Wyman, of the Public Health and Marine Hospital Service, from which I have extracted in the following chapter, will realise how great a difference in quarantine has been made by our present knowledge of yellow fever, in money, in time, in labour, in commercial injury, and in personal annoyance.

CHAPTER IX

THE VALUE OF DR. REED'S WORK TO THE WORLD

And the king said, What honour and dignity hath been done to Mordecai for this? Then said the king's servants that ministered to him, There is nothing done for him.
—ESTHER vi. 3.

NO consideration of Dr. Reed's life and work would be complete which did not place in high relief the suffering and sorrow from which he has freed mankind. I make no apologies, therefore, for describing as graphically as possible the horrors which occurred during epidemics of former times, in order to emphasise the fact that, thanks to the labours of Dr. Reed and his colleagues, the country need never be visited by another.

Between the years 1702 and 1878 yellow fever appeared in the United States, according to Keating, one hundred and twelve times, its invasions being most frequent and most destructive in the Southern States, although they reached as far north as Nantucket Island, Mass., where 259 persons died of it in 1763, a death rate, which, considering the small size of the island, must have represented a very high mortality.

The first epidemic concerning which we have reliable information is that which visited Philadelphia in 1793. This has been vividly described by Dr. Benjamin Rush, and by Mr. Mathew Carey, a member of the citizens' " Committee for Relieving the Sick and Distressed," both writing immediately after its cessation; and by La Roche, writing in 1855.

The epidemic began in August with a few scattered cases, which Rush tells us were so mild as not to excite suspicion of their real character. The first patient which Dr. Rush attended was the child of his friend, Dr. Hodge, whom he saw on the 5th of August, when he made a diagnosis of bilious fever. His suspicions were aroused, however, by several similar cases that followed, and on the 19th of the month he was called to a Mrs. Le Maigre, of Water Street, whose symptoms convinced him of the real character of the disease now rapidly increasing in the city, and he, in conjunction with certain other physicians, made known the condition of things to the College of Physicians. The first official notice of the disease took place on August 22, when the Mayor, Matthew Clarkson, wrote to the City Commissioners, giving the most peremptory orders as to the cleansing of the

servants abandoning tender and humane masters, who only wanted a little care to restore them to health and usefulness—who, I say, can even now think of these things without horror? . . .

A woman, whose husband and two children lay dead in the room with her, was seized with the pains of labour, without a mid-wife, or any other person to assist her. Her cries from the window brought up one of the carters employed by the committee for the relief of the sick. With his assistance she was delivered of a child, which died in a few minutes, as did the mother, who was utterly exhausted by her labour, by the disorder, and by the dreadful spectacle before her. And thus lay in one room no less than five dead bodies, an entire family, carried off in an hour or two.

In contrast to these painful scenes it should be mentioned that the city was never without many beautiful exhibitions of charity and humanity. One of these, which, although no greater than that of others, was perhaps more extensive in its results, was that of Stephen Girard, a native of France and a wealthy merchant of the city. He became so touched by the desolate condition of the patients in the public hospital at Bush-Hill that he offered to superintend the hospital management himself while the fever lasted, and a Pennsylvanian, Peter Helm, offered his services to the same end. No greater act of charity could have been shown, for the Bush-Hill Hospital was in a most deplorable condition described by Carey in vivid terms.

A profligate, abandoned set of nurses and attendants (hardly any of good character could at that time be procured) rioted on the provisions and comforts provided for the sick, who (unless at the hours when the doctors attended) were left almost entirely destitute of every assistance. The sick, the dying, and the dead were indiscriminately mingled together. Not the smallest appearance of order or regularity existed. It was, in fact, a great human slaughter house, where numerous victims were immolated at the altar of riot and intemperance. No wonder, then, that a general dread of the place prevailed through the city, and that a removal to it was considered as the seal of death. In consequence there were various instances of sick persons locking their rooms and resisting every effort to carry them away. At length the poor were so much afraid of being sent to Bush-Hill that they would not acknowledge their illness until it was no longer possible to conceal it. For it is to be observed that the fear of contagion was so prevalent that as soon as anyone was taken sick an alarm was spread among the neighbours and every effort was used to have the sick person hurried off to Bush-Hill, to avoid spreading the disorder. The cases of poor people forced in this way to the hospital, though labouring only under common colds and common fall fevers, are numerous and afflicting.   .   .   .

But the case was soon altered under the direction of the managers, Girard and Helm. They in-

Coates, the father of eight, and Mr. Benjamin Scull and Mr. John Morell, both fathers of ten children. They were all in imminent danger, but it pleased God to make me the instrument of saving each of their lives. . . . Every moment in the intervals of my visits to the sick was employed in prescribing in my own house for the poor, or in sending answers to messages from my patients. Time was now too precious (October) to be spent in counting the number of persons who called upon me for advice. From circumstances I believe it was frequently 150, and seldom less than 50 a day for five or six weeks. The evening did not bring with it the least relaxation from my labours. I received letters every day from the country and from distant parts of the Union containing inquiries into the mode of treating the disease, and after the health and lives of persons who had remained in the city. The business of every evening was to answer these letters and also to write to my family. To these constant labours of body and mind were added distress from a variety of causes. Having found myself unable to comply with the numerous applications that were made to me, I was obliged to refuse many every day. My sister counted forty-seven in one forenoon before eleven o'clock. Many of them left my door with tears, but they did not feel more distress than I did from refusing to follow them. . . . In riding through the streets I was often forced to resist the entreaties of parents imploring a visit to their children, or of children to their parents. I recollect, and even *yet* with pain, that I tore myself away at one time from five persons in Moravian Alley who attempted to stop me, by suddenly whipping my horse and driving my chair as speedily as possible beyond the reach of their cries.

But I had other afflictions besides the distress which arose from the abortive sympathy which I have just described. On the 11th of September my ingenuous pupil, Mr. Washington, fell a victim to his humanity. . . . Scarce had I recovered from the shock of the death of this amiable youth when I was called to weep for another pupil, Mr. Alston, who died in my neighbourhood the next day. . . . At this time a third pupil, Mr. Fisher, was ill in my house. On the 26th of the month Mr. Coxe, my only assistant, was seized with the fever and went to his grandfather's. I followed him with a look which I feared would be the last in my house. At two o'clock my sister, who had complained for several days, yielded to the disease and retired to her bed. My mother followed her, much indisposed, early in the evening. My black servant man had been confined with the fever for several days, and had, on that day, for the first time quitted his bed. My little mulatto boy, of eleven years old, was the only person in my family who was able to afford me the least assistance. . . .

On the 1st of October, at two o'clock, my sister died. I got into my carriage within an hour after she expired and spent the afternoon in visiting patients. According as a sense of duty or of grief has predominated in my mind I have approved of this act or not, ever since. She had borne a share in my labours. She had been my nurse in sickness, and my casuist in my choice of duties. My whole heart reposed itself in her friendship. . . . From this time I declined in health and strength. All motion was painful to me. My appetite began to fail. My night sweats continued. My short and imperfect sleep was disturbed with distressing or frightful dreams.

The scenes of them were derived altogether from sick rooms and graveyards. . . . For the first two weeks after I visited patients in the yellow fever I carried a rag wetted with vinegar and smelled it occasionally in sick rooms, but as I saw and felt the signs of the universal presence of miasmata in my system I laid aside this and all other precautions. I rested myself on the bedsides of my patients, and I drank milk or ate fruit in their rooms. Besides being saturated with miasmata I had another security against being infected in sick rooms, and that was, I went into scarcely a house which was more infected than my own. Many of the poor people who called upon me for treatment were bled by my pupils in my shop and in the yard, which is between it and the street. From the want of a sufficient number of bowls to receive the blood it was sometimes suffered to flow and putrefy upon the ground. From this source streams of miasmata were constantly poured into my house and conveyed to my body by the air during every hour of the day and night. . . . My perception of the lapse of time was new to me. It was uncommonly slow. The ordinary business and pursuits of men appeared to me in a light that was equally new. The hearse and the grave mingled themselves with every view I took of human affairs. Under these impressions I recollect being as much struck with observing a number of men employed in digging the cellar of a large house as I should have been at any other time in seeing preparations for building a palace upon a cake of ice. I recollect, further, being struck with surprise, about the first of October, in seeing a man busily employed in laying in wood for the approaching winter. I should as

soon have thought of making provision for a dinner
on the first day of the year 1800.

After the loss of my health I received letters from
friends in the country, pressing me in the strongest terms
to leave the city. Such a step had become impracticable.
My aged mother was too infirm to be removed, and I
could not leave her. I was, moreover, part of a little
circle of physicians who had associated themselves in
support of the new remedies. This circle would have
been broken up by my quitting the city. The weather
varied the disease, and in the weakest state of the body
I expected to be able, from the reports of my pupils,
to assist my associates in detecting its changes and in
accommodating our remedies to them. Under these circumstances it pleased God to enable me to reply to one
of the letters that urged my retreat from the city that
I had resolved to stick to my principles, my practice,
and my patients to the last extremity.

From the 15th of October the disease gradually
declined, and by December the city was free from
the pestilence, so that the 12th of that month was
observed as a day of thanksgiving. The total number of deaths, reckoned from the burial lists, was
4041, and as the city during the epidemic contained
40,144 inhabitants, it was literally decimated.
Much difference existed among physicians as to
the manner in which the disease originated. To
our enlightened minds it would appear to have
been imported by some refugees from San Do-

mingo who arrived in Philadelphia during the latter part of July. It is true that no cases of yellow fever were reported as occurring among them, but then it is expressly stated that the first cases which came under notice were so mild as to escape recognition, and that their nature only became known after others of a well-marked character developed; it seems probable, therefore, that the imported cases were of the same indefinite character and their real nature was never known. The transmission of the disease becomes perfectly intelligible when we read the remark, made casually by Dr. Rush, that "Moschetoes (the usual attendants of a sickly season) were uncommonly numerous." Some excellent physicians held by the theory of importation, even though they do not seem to have focussed their suspicions upon the San Domingo refugees; there were not wanting, however, persons of high authority, of whom Dr. Rush himself was one, who insisted that the disease was generated within the city, and Dr. Rush was of opinion that a large quantity of coffee which had been allowed to decay upon one of the wharves was the whole cause of the trouble. So convinced, indeed, was he that the disease arose from this cause that he published a short address in one of the daily papers, describing the exact spot where the coffee lay and warning all persons to avoid the locality.

I must not neglect to mention here one lay account of this epidemic, which is of peculiar interest. The horrors of that frightful summer appealed to the weird imagination of the first American romancer, the precursor of Hawthorne, Charles Brockden Brown (1771-1810). The misery and death in the stricken city furnish a lurid background for the happenings of his sombre story, "Arthur Mervyn." The result is a work of fiction containing the most vivid description we have of the ravages of yellow fever in earlier times.

During the next eighty years the United States was visited by yellow fever every year, with one exception, 1861, in which no deaths were reported from any quarter. During this period two great epidemics occurred, one in New Orleans in 1853, and another in Norfolk in 1855. I will not pause to dwell on these, but pass on to that terrible visitation which is within the memory of most of us, the epidemic of 1878 in Memphis and its vicinity. The history of this terrible pestilence has been written in the most graphic manner by Mr. J. M. Keating in a volume, now unfortunately out of print, entitled "History of the Yellow Fever Epidemic of 1878 in Memphis, Tenn."

The pestilence in this instance began as early as May, when a steamboat, the *Sudder,* entered Memphis with a case of yellow fever on board.

The disease spread slowly at first and created little alarm until August, but by the middle of that month the city was in a state of panic and everyone who could, began to escape.

Men, women, and children [says Keating], poured out of the city by every possible avenue of escape. . . . Out by the country roads to the little hamlets and plantations, where many of them were welcome guests in happier days; out by every possible conveyance—by hacks, by carriages, buggies, waggons, furniture vans, and street-drays; away by bateaux, by anything that could float on the river; and by the railroads, the trains on which, especially on the Louisville road, were so packed as to make the trip to that city, or to Cincinnati, a positive torture to many delicate women every mile of the way. The aisles of the cars were filled and the platforms packed. In vain the railroad officials plead, in vain they increased the accommodations. The stream of passengers seemed to be endless and they were as mad as they were many. The ordinary courtesies of life were ignored, politeness gave way to selfishness, and the desire for personal safety broke through all social amenities. . . . To the cities of the far North and the far West they fled, too many of them to die on the way like dogs, neglected and shunned, as if cursed of God; or, to reach the wished-for goal, only to die, a plague to all about, carrying dismay to those who even then were busying themselves for the relief of the stricken cities of the South. In less than ten days, by the 24th of August, twenty-five thousand people had left the city and in two weeks after five thousand others were in camp, leaving a little less than twenty thousand to face consequences they could not escape. . . .

By the last week in August the panic was over in the city. All had fled who could, and all were in camp who would go. There were then, it was estimated, about three thousand cases of fever . . . an appalling gloom hung over the doomed city. At night it was silent as the grave, by day it seemed desolate as the desert. There were hours, especially at night, when the solemn oppression of universal death bore upon the human mind, as if the day of judgment was about to dawn. Not a sound was to be heard; the silence was painfully profound. Death prevailed everywhere. Trade and traffic were suspended. The energies of all who remained were engaged in the struggle with death. The poor were reduced to beggary, and even the rich gladly accepted alms. . . Even the animals felt the oppression and fled from the city. Rats, cats, or dogs were not to be seen. Death was everywhere triumphant. White women were seldom to be met with, children never. The voice of prayer was lifted up only at the bed of pain or death, or in some home circle where anguish was supreme and death threatened, as in a few cases he accomplished, total annihilation. Tears for one loved one were choked by the feeling of uncertainty provoked by the sad condition of another. In one case a family of four was found dead in one room, the bodies partially decomposed. There were no public evidences of sorrow. The wife was borne to the tomb while the husband was unconscious of his loss, and whole families were swept away in such quick succession that not one had knowledge of the other's departure. Death dealt kindly by these. . . . Neither cleanliness nor right living were a shield to stay the hand of the destroyer. He invaded the homes of the most chaste and the den of the vilest. He took innocence and infamy at the same moment and spread terror everywhere. Where sorrow was so general there could be no parade of it. There were no funerals and but little demand for funeral services. The luxuries of woe were dispensed with. In most cases the driver of the hearse and an assistant composed the funeral party. Not infrequently many bodies were left in the cemetery unburied for a night, so hard pressed were the managers for labour, and so numerous were the demands upon what they had. . . . The churches were closed. The congregations dispersed. The members were far apart. Some were safe, many were dead. Only a few survived, and these were manifesting their faith by works. The police were cut down from forty-one to seven. Their ranks were recruited and again were thinned. They were a second and a third time filled up, and yet death was relentless. He was jealous of all sway but his own.

I have so far dwelt solely upon the misery and sorrow directly attendant on the march of the pestilence, but the worst horrors following in its train arose from the lawlessness and criminality which always come to light and run riot under such conditions, when human nature throws off all disguise and stands forth *human*.

Petty thieving [says Keating] prevailed as an epidemic. This was principally confined to food and clothing, and wood or coal, or both. A few who came to nurse died, leaving full trunks of silverware, bijouterie, bric-a-brac, and clothes, to prove how industriously they could ply two trades and make one cover up and supply the deficiencies of the other. A few of them also made themselves notorious for lewdness and drunkenness. To these vices many deaths were due. They shocked decency and outraged humanity, they were no better than the beasts of the field. Male and female they herded together in vileness. They made of the epidemic a carnival. . . . One of these, a woman who would not or could not control her appetite for strong drink, while stupefied from wine and brandy allowed a poor woman to leave her bed, naked as when born, and wander out into the country one inclement night, calling as she went for the husband who had preceded her to the grave by a few days. . . . In the house of an ex-judge, whence a whole family had been borne to the grave, the victims of neglect, four such nurses died, and in the trunks of one, the worst of them, a woman of seeming refinement, there was found the family plate and wearing apparel of the judge's wife, then absent in Ohio. This woman and her paramours fell victims to the fever which they invited by their debauchery and hastened by their excesses. In the whole range of human depravity there are few parallels to these cases. They illustrate the extremes of degradation; they sounded the lowest depths of vice and shamed even the standards of savage life.

But it was not only among the lowest and vilest that the dark side of human nature was brought

took place in the epidemic of 1793, and I wish space permitted me to do justice to many others.

In the pestilence of 1878 the whole country seemed to be moved with compassion. "The cry for food," says Keating, "for clothing, for money, for doctors, for as many as a thousand coffins, went out by telegraph to the ends of the earth, and a prompt and generous response came back. By telegraph, by express, through the banks, by private hands, money was forwarded by hundreds, by thousands of dollars—New York City alone sending altogether $43,800. . . . The people of the North were especially urgent; it seemed as though they could not do enough. 'We send,' they said, 'what we can; but you, who know what you need, must ask—"Ask and ye shall receive."' The Republic in its remotest confines was moved as if by a divine impulse. The leading artists of the lyric as well as of the dramatic stage were especially conspicuous in good gifts, in generous contributions. . . . The miner in the Nevada hills, the ranchero in far California, and the farmer in distant Oregon vied in dispensing a charity equal to the growing exigencies of the time, while the people of the older States of the East, where organisations existed in every city and village, were eagerly engaged in the good Samaritan's work. . . . Hundreds of men and women volunteered

as nurses, who were destined to a speedy death.
. . . A long line of graves in Elmwood Cemetery tells the story of their fidelity to a mission that
was one purely of mercy and loving kindness."

Instances of individual self-sacrifice were as
numerous as in former years and they were conspicuous among those whose lives would have least
suggested it. "One unfortunate 'woman of the
town,'" says Keating, "a phrase which only too
well tells her trade, gave up her house to be used
as a hospital, and herself, until she fell in the act,
nursed the sick, and closed the eyes and covered the
faces of the dead. Others, doomed like her to become a curse instead of a blessing to humanity,
followed her example. One such came from a
great city of the West, disguised as a widow, and
faithfully and assiduously continued to do her duty,
running the gauntlet of death every hour: even
when all like her were denounced in her presence
as irreclaimable and abandoned of God by an
earnest Christian woman, whom she nursed to convalescence."

A word must be said here of the good accomplished by the organisation called the Howard
Association, after the great philanthropist, John
Howard. The first of these associations was established in Memphis during a comparatively
mild epidemic of yellow fever which occurred

dry goods boxes were utilised; they were piled one on top of the other and fastened with ropes to the bed of the waggons. Negroes were procured for this work; they were known to rob the dead and the vacant residences. The following winter several visits were made to the cabins, where clothing, silver, and other valuables were found. On one occasion of this kind I was called by the town marshal to identify some things supposed to have been taken from our house; while looking down on a crowd of negroes I called the marshal's attention to a negro man wearing my father's hat. He proved to be a minister, and we found a waggon-load of various articles at his house. The negroes' work as grave-diggers proved to be very poor, as sixteen inches was afterwards found to be the depth of any grave made during that time.

From a possible recurrence of horrors such as these we are now insured by the labours of Walter Reed and his colleagues, who risked their lives to ascertain the facts by which we are now protected. The reports of the Army Commission on yellow fever are so modest and self-restrained that they give little or no idea of the dangers to which the members were incessantly exposed, nor of the painful scenes which they were daily called upon to witness. I quote, therefore, again from Mrs. Warner's letter, for it is due to both the living and the dead that the full extent of their efforts should be known.

From the date of a lecture I heard on yellow fever delivered by Dr. R. B. Maury and Dr. R. W. Mitchell, I was possessed of a great desire to come in contact with the disease. When our Government called for volunteer nurses to go to Cuba I availed myself of this opportunity.

In August, 1900, I was ordered from Matanzas to Havana. The night before my transfer to Havana I was entertained at the quarters of the officers of the 2nd Cavalry stationed at Matanzas; there I met a Major Cartwright, who informed me that he also had been ordered to Havana, as he was an immune, having had the fever in '98 at Santiago. Two weeks after my arrival at the yellow fever camp the ambulance brought a patient from General Lee's headquarters, and as I stepped forward to give directions in regard to him I recognised Major Cartwright. After some conversation he stated that he could not possibly have yellow fever, as he certainly had a genuine case in '98. However, on the sixth day after his arrival he died of black vomit. Major Peterson also thought that he had had the fever, but he was taken ill again with it, and his wife, hearing of his illness, two hours after his death, committed suicide by shooting herself through the temple in our quarters at Las Animas.

The only nurse with me who had yellow fever was one that claimed to be an immune; she was sent to Major Edmund's residence at Quemados the night before his death; she returned to the camp and four days after was taken with a mild case. We had no mosquitoes in our camp.

Quarantine was very strict, but we continued to have yellow fever among the soldiers and officers; we were poorly equipped at Columbia Barracks Detention Camp, and yet the mortality was not so great as in this country. A few officers and privates from the Palace in Havana were taken to Las Animas, a Cuban hospital for civilians under Major Gorgas' supervision; he called on our chief surgeon for help and I was ordered there for ten days. At this place they were well equipped, the nurses being well cared for as well as the patients. We lost that week Major Peterson, Captain Page, the quartermaster sergeant, one soldier, and one civilian employé. Major Gorgas was very successful in the treatment of the fever, and upon my return to Camp Columbia I determined to imitate his directions.

In September I nursed Dr. James Carroll, a member of Major Reed's staff of Commissioners, and he told me he experimented upon himself with the mosquito; while he had a severe case he did not have hæmorrhages, but even to the whites of his eyes he was as yellow as saffron. A few days after Dr. Carroll's chill Dr. Jesse Lazear was stricken with the fever. He also was a member of the board and was brought on a litter to our camp about eleven A. M. He knew what his illness was and informed me that he had his chill about six P. M.; he had not been in bed all night, as he was busy writing up their experiments in regard to yellow fever and the mosquito. His temperature was 103°, his pulse 80; he lived five days; the black vomit would spurt from his mouth up through the bar over his cot. I had just relieved the day nurse and gone on for the night; my efforts to keep him in bed failed and I called for help, but before assistance reached me we had made several turns around the room in his efforts to get out. All night it took two men to hold him, and he died the next morning.

In December I met Major Reed, and it was at this time that they had begun in earnest to erect buildings for the special experiments to prove that the mosquito was the only source of infection. Major Reed was an officer to whom we were all devoted; he liked best to be called " Doctor." I was always glad on my daily visits to the laboratory to catch him there; he had won the friendship and esteem of the entire corps, having the most genial manners and was so considerate and kind to everyone. I do not feel that I could speak in too high terms of Major Reed. At all times he was so willing to go into details with any part of the experiment I did not comprehend, and was patient enough to give me a peep through the different microscopes and give a full explanation. I told him of our '78 epidemic, and he informed me that Surgeon-General Sternberg was in Memphis at that time. The experimental camp was called after Dr. Lazear. In a statement I heard Major Reed make, he said that Dr. Lazear's efforts in this work had been of vast importance. Major Reed was strong in his friendships, as Dr. Carroll can readily testify. I recall an incident which gives an insight into the kind of man he was. On one occasion he moved his mess quarters because he heard his brother officers use language at the table which was very ungentlemanly. It was due to his indefatigable efforts that we owe our success with yellow fever at Camp Lazear, as we never lost a case experimented upon.

To give an idea of the frightful mortality of this disease in actual numbers, I turn to the paper issued by Reed and Carroll in 1901, on "The Prevention of Yellow Fever."[3]

It would be difficult to determine with accuracy the loss of life occasioned by the ninety-five invasions of our territory by yellow fever during the past two hundred and eight years. We have endeavoured to collect from the most available sources the mortality caused by the disease, but have been unable to obtain any reliable data for the earlier epidemics. If we confine ourselves to the epidemics which have occurred since 1793, we find that there have not been less than 100,000 deaths from this cause. The greatest sufferer has been the city of New Orleans, with 41,348 deaths, followed by the city of Philadelphia with 10,038 deaths. The epidemics of 1855, 1873, 1878, and 1879 claimed 7759 victims in the city of Memphis, Tenn. From 1800 to 1876 Charleston lost 4565 of its citizens by attacks of yellow fever. New York during the earlier and later invasions of this disease has had 3454 deaths, while the later epidemic of 1855 in Norfolk, Va., caused over 2000 deaths. During our brief occupation of the Island of Cuba (July, 1898-December, 1900), with every precaution brought into exercise to ward off the disease, there have occurred among the officers and men of our army 1575 cases of yellow fever, with 231 deaths. If we reckon the average mortality at 20 per cent. there have not been less than 500,000 cases of

[3] "The Prevention of Yellow Fever." Med. Rec., Oct. 26, 1901.

yellow fever in the United States during the period
from 1793 to 1900.

Yet the actual loss of life from the disease, appalling as it is, is but a part of the distress which
it has occasioned to the country. The pecuniary
loss, both direct and indirect, is a matter of serious
moment. Estimates of the exact amount of money
loss in epidemics are hard to arrive at, since
account must be taken not only of actual expendi-
tures in the relief or restriction of an epidemic, but
also of the commercial loss resulting from the interruption of intercourse with the afflicted region
and the maintenance of the necessary quarantine
regulations. I have, however, collected an amount
of information sufficient to demonstrate conclusively the heaviness of the loss, although it is somewhat miscellaneous in character.

Keating states that the amount contributed by
the world at large for the relief of the stricken cities
of the South in 1878 was $4,548,703. Dr. Horl-
beck, chairman of the committee appointed in
1897 to investigate the ætiology of yellow fever,
states in his report that the total loss to the country
in the 1878 epidemic was not less than $100,000,000.
The loss to the city of New Orleans alone was
over $10,000,000. Evidence given before a Con-
gressional Committee in 1897 disclosed the fact

that the loss incurred by the Southern Pacific Railway Company in Texas and Louisiana during the epidemic of 1897 was in excess of one million of dollars. So strongly has our national prosperity always been affected through commercial losses occasioned by the disease that the probability of their arising from *the introduction of yellow fever into our Southern States was in former years considered a serious obstacle to the annexation of Cuba.* In 1889. Dr. Benjamin Lee, then president of the State Board of Health of Louisiana, read before the association a paper with the title, " Do the Sanitary Interests of the United States Demand the Annexation of Cuba?" in which this sentence occurs: "A single widespread epidemic of yellow fever would cost the United States more in money, to say nothing of the grief and misery which it would entail, than the purchase of Cuba." In forcible comparison with this statement are the words of General Leonard Wood, spoken at the memorial service in honour of Dr. Reed. " I know of no man," he said, " who has done so much for humanity as Major Reed. His discovery results in the saving of more lives annually than were lost in the Cuban war and saves the commercial interests of the world a greater financial loss in each year than the cost of the entire Cuban war." When we look back over our history in the immediate past and remember that our occupation of Cuba was (let us hope at least to some extent) actuated by dictates of humanity which forbade us to leave the people we had freed unprotected and undeveloped, we realise that we have our reward, in our deliverance from the very evil which we were supposed to entail upon ourselves in thus fulfilling our duty to our neighbour.

Another source of expense to the country against which we are now insured, is that involved in keeping up expensive quarantine regulations, now shown to be, to a large extent, unnecessary. I have no means of estimating the direct cost of these, but some idea of it may be formed from a little volume on United States Quarantine Regulations, issued in 1889 by Surgeon-General Walter Wyman. After considering the nature of yellow fever and stating directions for ordering life in the manner most likely to escape it, he proceeds to consider at length the following subjects: disinfection of houses; disinfection of baggage; isolation of infected cases; detention camps; disinfection of premises; disinfection of freight; inspection of trains; regulation of traffic; disinfection of mail; inspection of mail; inspection of vessels; disinfection of vessels; inspection of territory. When the cost of carrying out all these measures in detail is considered, it is plain that protection against

yellow fever, according to the old ideas, was a
heavy expense to Government. But nearly all
of these procedures were instituted to meet the
theory of infection by fomites, and now that this
is disproved all expedients based upon it are unnecessary. The few precautions really essential are
those given by Dr. Reed, which we have already
quoted (see Chapter VII), and we need only compare these with the long list of measures just cited
to realise what a burden of expense and annoyance
is removed from the shoulders of Government.

And now let us pause for a moment to ascertain
what has been done by the world at large in appreciation of the man who has accomplished so
much in the service of his fellow-creatures. Let
us inquire, with the motto of this chapter, "What
honour and dignity hath been bestowed upon Mordecai for this?"

The members of Dr. Reed's own profession, as
well as medical societies and learned bodies, both
at home and abroad, have spared no exertions to
show their satisfaction in the distinction he has
conferred upon his profession; and his friends and
acquaintances, both medical and lay, have shown
a generous and loving spirit of appreciation in
the Memorial Association established by them to
secure that some practical return should be made
for his services to mankind. But these demonstra-

tions, right and fitting as they are, represent only a small part of what is due. Acknowledgment of Dr. Reed's services to humanity should not be confined to his colleagues and friends. It is the nation which he has benefited and the government he has served from whom it is due; not as a favour, nor even as a recompense, but as a testimonial of enduring gratitude.

"Yet popular appreciation of the value of the work of the yellow fever commission has been," so says Major Kean, "singularly slow and imperfect. While nearly every educated person in the United States is familiar with the name and work of a distinguished Austrian surgeon who has recently demonstrated in this country an operation for the cure of a rather rare deformity in childhood, only a small fraction of them know anything of Walter Reed, the conqueror of the 'yellow plague.'"

"Precedents are abundant," Major Kean continues, "for State aid to public benefactors and their families. The English Government a century ago, when the purchasing value of money was far greater than at present, gave to Jenner, the discoverer of vaccination, grants amounting to £30,-000. He also received £7383 from a subscription in India. Pasteur, the founder of the science of bacteriology, besides numerous honours and decorations and money donations from other sources, appointment in Washington as professor of bacteriology and clinical microscopy in the Army Medical School and another as professor of pathology and bacteriology in the Columbian University. To his work in these institutions he now devoted the greater part of his time, and during the brief remainder of his life he was occupied mainly in teaching, a line of work for which his natural abilities seem to have been no less marked than they were elsewhere.

Dr. A. F. A. King speaks of Dr. Reed's success as a teacher thus:

In the whole domain of knowledge there is probably no subject more difficult and intricate than that of pathology, especially when considered in relation with bacteriology, this latter being also a comparatively new departure, and therefore bristling with the unfamiliar terms of a new and laboured nomenclature, as every new science necessarily must be.

Notwithstanding these difficulties, Professor Reed, with his well-trained mind and cultivated powers of observation, inspired, too, with the spirit of research and led on by the charm of discovering new principles and new facts, had devoted himself with so much ardour, earnestness, and industry to the study of his chosen sphere of thought that it may be said all difficulties had been trampled under his feet; that he rose, step by step, to higher and still higher planes of knowledge, until he reached an eminence where the whole subject became easily intelligible in one comprehensive view and where he himself attained a complete mastery of his favourite theme.

Having traversed the highways of knowledge himself, he was fully able to lead his pupils along the same paths and perhaps point out to them many short cuts which were easier than the longer distances and more laborious journeys originally pursued by himself. It should be remembered also that many of these roads were not always the well-travelled avenues of old lines of thought, but, on the contrary, entirely new, strange, and perhaps lonely ways, far out on the prairies of investigation, where briars of speculation, weeds of error, and the *ignes fatui* of false theories were liable to obstruct and mislead the honest seeker for truth. It was under these circumstances that Professor Reed became a trusted guide and counsellor. In these trackless wastes of thought he could not easily get lost or take a wrong direction, for in many instances he was able to say: "*I made these paths myself,*" and he well knew whither they would lead.

A pupil of his, Captain J. Hamilton Stone, Assistant Surgeon, U. S. A., writes of him as follows:

As a teacher Dr. Reed always seemed to me to be first of all, master of his theme. His information was so much his own—a part of him, as it were—that when it was given to others it flowed forth with unadulterated naturalness, and sparkled with a keen interest which his charming personality could not help but lend it. These qualities would not permit his words to fall upon deaf ears. His kindly and considerate mien, together with his universally acknowledged high scien-

A friend who saw him during the summer of 1902 says: "He was very much worn by his scientific labours, and it was also evident that he felt most keenly the attempts which were being made by persons in authority to rob him of his just fame for the work which he had done." To a nature so generous and affectionate as Dr. Reed's, the hardest part of such annoyances must have lain in the pain caused by the betrayal of those in whom his trusting nature placed entire confidence, and this was probably a harder trial to him than the risk of losing any part of the distinction he had earned, for, as his wife says, "When his great work was accomplished, the happiness which filled his soul was entirely for the suffering he would spare humanity. He rejoiced that he had not lived in vain, and that God had seen fit to make him an instrument of good."

But, although Dr. Reed had his share of misunderstanding to endure, his work was not without recognition of the most gratifying description. In the summer of 1902 Harvard University bestowed on him the honorary degree of M. A., conferred by President Eliot in these words: "Walter Reed, graduate of the University of Virginia, the army surgeon who planned and directed in Cuba the experiments which have given man control over that fearful scourge, yellow fever." In this connection

I give a letter of Dr. Reed's to Dr. Theobald Smith, now of Harvard, which shows in a simple, unaffected manner his pleasure in the distinction he had just received, and also gives evidence that his interest in the question of yellow fever was as keen as it had ever been.

SURGEON-GENERAL'S OFFICE, WASHINGTON,
July 18, 1902.

MY DEAR DR. SMITH:

On returning to the city from a short outing, I find your kind favour of the 8th instant. I am, of course, extremely interested in what you tell me about the agglutinative reactions of *b. icteroides* and hog-cholera. Carroll and I, as you know, in testing the blood of yellow fever and hog-cholera had found that whenever a given specimen would clump *icteroides,* it would affect hog-cholera in like manner. With a culture of hog-cholera from Welch's laboratory we got clumping with *icteroides* serum in less dilution than with *b. icteroides*. We only tested this particular serum with this one culture of hog-culture. As to the significance of this clumping, I have not doubted the very close affinity of these micro-organisms ever since I found that *b. icteroides* (orig.) when fed to young swine would produce a fatal infection with the acute lesions of hog-cholera.

Concerning your inquiry whether there is virulent hog-cholera in Cuba, I think that I can safely answer, Yes. Agramonte and other physicians assured me that this disease was well known on the island and that, in certain years, it caused a high mortality among swine. I did not see the disease, as I made no attempt to do so, but I think you can safely accept its presence there. The domestic relations between the lower classes and the swine are as intimate as can be found among dwellers in the same house and often in the same room. Whether *b. icteroides* produces a disease *sui generis* in the West Indies, I cannot say. It is probably responsible for occasional fatal infections with continued fever.

Thank you so much for your kind congratulations on the Harvard degree. Of course I didn't deserve it, but I could not altogether repress a feeling of pride in finding myself in such distinguished company.

Sincerely yours,
WALTER REED.

Shortly after this the degree of LL.D. was conferred on him by the University of Michigan.

In October, 1902, when Dr. Reed returned to Washington for the winter, it became evident that his strength was much below par. Each evening he came home worn out with fatigue, the lines of exhaustion on his face telling plainly that the day's work had been too much for his powers. All mental exertion became a painful effort to him, and he complained frequently to his wife of the difficulty he experienced in giving his accustomed lectures. One night, as he was leaving the house for the Columbia Lecture Hall, he glanced over his notes, and shaking his head, remarked, " I cannot realise that I ever delivered this lecture. It is utterly beyond my mental capacity now." Before his friends and acquaintances he exerted himself to keep up his usual flow of spirits, but his wife, to whom he could express himself without restraint, was so shocked at the change wrought in him by a few short weeks that she became oppressed by the sense of an impending calamity. The faithful old messenger at the Museum was the only person besides his wife to whom he allowed himself to give way, and to him he said one day, " Beechner, I am a very sick man."

On Wednesday, the 12th of November, Dr. Reed returned from his office earlier than usual, and remarked to his wife that he must have eaten something at luncheon which had disagreed with him. He was so ill throughout the remainder of the day that he could not go to his lecture in the evening, and the next day he remained in bed most of the forenoon. Later he rose, dressed, and went out, although still complaining of abdominal pain which caused him to limp. On Friday, the 14th, he consulted his old friend and brother officer, Major W. C. Borden, stating that he himself thought the trouble was appendicitis.

On examination, Major Borden found a tender spot, one-third of the way inward from the right anterior superior spine, with increased muscular tension in the neighbourhood. The temperature was then 99.4° and the pulse 77. Dr. Borden made a diagnosis of appendicitis, but as Dr. Reed was much better next morning, it was hoped the worst was over. That night the temperature was 99.8° and the next morning it was 98°. Dr. Reed sat up in bed most of that day (Sunday, the 16th), begged for solid food, read his letters, talked of the improvements to be made at his country home in the spring, saw some of his old friends, and was altogether so well and bright that he seemed on the high road to recovery. On Sunday evening, however, his temperature rose to 100.4°, with some return of pain, and although the other symptoms were not worse, Dr. Borden advised operation as soon as possible the following day. Early the next morning, accordingly, Dr. Reed was taken to the Army Hospital Barracks, where Dr. Borden operated at eleven A. M. Just before the operation Dr. Reed said to his old friend, Major Kean, to whom he was much attached, " Kean, I am not afraid of the knife, but if anything should happen to me, I am leaving my wife and daughter so little;" and as he went under the influence of the ether he was heard to whisper, " So little, so little."

Some difficulty was encountered in finding the appendix, so that it was necessary to enlarge the incision, and when located, it proved to be very large and closely adherent to the caput coli. The organ was partly filled with pus and had perfo-

rated at one point, but the pus had not escaped into
the abdominal cavity on account of a thin wall of
adhesions. During the separation of these adhesions pus escaped, but as it was carefully taken up
with a dry sponge, Dr. Borden believed that none
escaped into the abdomen. As the appendix was so
necrotic at the base that no invagination of the
stump was possible, it was simply ligated. Gauze
drainage was inserted, the lower end of the drain
being carefully packed over the stump down into
the space between the posterior abdominal wall
and lower end of the cæcum where the pus had
gravitated. The appendix, itself, on examination
showed evidence of considerable previous inflam-
mation, and it became plain that certain attacks of
" indigestion " and " intestinal colic," from which
Dr. Reed had suffered occasionally for some years,
had been, in reality, mild attacks of appendicitis.

The overwork and anxiety which Dr. Reed had
borne so cheerfully during previous years had their
effect now. He reacted badly from the operation,
the nausea continuing for nearly eighteen hours,
and even after this was relieved he suffered from
almost uncontrollable nervousness and great depression.

His friend, Major Kean, who saw him every day
during his illness, found him still anxious to a
painful degree as to the future of his family. His

The quotation is taken from President Eliot's address when he conferred upon Dr. Reed the Harvard honorary degree, a distinction in which Dr. Reed took such especial pleasure that it seems peculiarly fitting it should mark his last resting place. A very successful marble bust of Dr. Reed, by the young sculptor, Hans Schuler, has recently been placed in the Surgeon-General's Library in Washington.

The news of Dr. Reed's untimely death was received by his profession and by the scientific world at large with poignant regret. The loss of such a man, at the zenith of his usefulness, with powers undimmed, and a future full of possibilities, was a bereavement which reached far beyond his own immediate circle and occasioned a national regret. Expressions of grief, and of sympathy for his family, came freely from every side, couched in terms of the most genuine feeling.

The New York Academy of Medicine, the University of Virginia, Columbia University, the American Academy of Medicine, the International Congress of Medicine, and many other scientific bodies at home and abroad passed resolutions expressing their sense of the loss sustained by the profession and their sympathy for Dr. Reed's family. The Medical Society of the District of Columbia, of which Dr. Reed had been a distin-

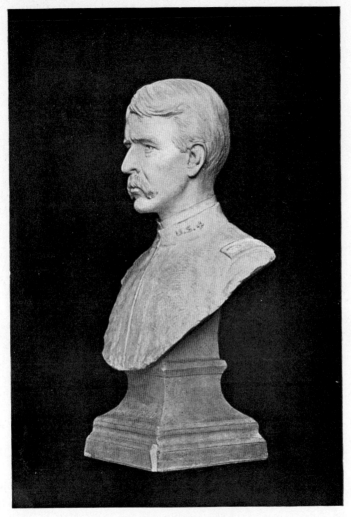

MAJOR WALTER REED

Bust by Hans Schuler.   Now in the library of the Surgeon-General
in Washington

guished member, held a memorial service on December 31, 1902, at which some of his friends and brother officers spoke on different aspects of his life and work. I have already quoted largely from the addresses made on this occasion, and I will pause here only to emphasise one point which strikes the reader forcibly in all of them, namely, the note of personal feeling apparent under the most conventional forms of expression. It would seem as though no one could come in contact with Dr. Reed without experiencing the charm and force of his personality in a lasting manner, so that even those whose knowledge of him was limited to a passing acquaintance experienced a sense of individual loss on hearing he was gone.

All of the leading medical journals published expressions of appreciation of Dr. Reed's work and grief for his untimely end. One of these, in particular, by Dr. George Nuttall in the Journal of Hygiene for April, 1903, contains an interesting account of his work and a warm-hearted defence of his claims to distinction against his detractors.

During the winter following Dr. Reed's death a strong desire arose among his friends as to the establishment of some memorial in his honour. The project first assumed definite shape at a dinner given by Professor Alexander Graham Bell to a number of the members of the Association of

CHAPTER XI

THE OTHER MEMBERS OF THE YELLOW FEVER COMMISSION

And there some whom a thirst
Ardent, unquenchable, fires,
Not with the crowd to be spent,
Not without aim to go round
In an eddy of purposeless dust,
Effort unmeaning and vain.
　　　　—MATTHEW ARNOLD, *Rugby Chapel.*

IT would not be fitting that this volume should close without special mention of the men associated with Dr. Reed in his experimental work. It is true that " his was the master mind and he the guiding spirit," but his three associates gave themselves to the cause with no less devotion than he; two of them suffered from the disease, and one lost his life by it. If the pestilence at our gates has been stayed by the efforts of the Commission, ought we not to honour these " brave soldiers in the Liberation War of Humanity," by whom the victory has been gained, only less than their commander?

JAMES CARROLL

Dr. James Carroll was born at Woolwich, England, on June 5, 1854. He received a good com-

mon school education, and when he was fifteen
emigrated to Canada, where for some years he
lived the life of a backwoodsman. In 1874 he
entered the United States Army and afterwards,
while still a soldier, he began the study of medicine at the University of the City of New York,
during the session of 1886-1887. After the break
of a year he resumed his medical studies in Baltimore, at the University of Maryland, in 1889-1891,
and received his degree from that institution. During the winters of 1891-1892 and 1892-1893 he
undertook some post-graduate work at the Johns
Hopkins Hospital in pathology and bacteriology.

His first association with Dr. Reed was in 1893,
when he was assigned to duty at the Army Medical
School in Washington, and they continued to be
more or less connected during the next six years.
In 1899, as I have related elsewhere, they were
both appointed by Surgeon-General Sternberg to
investigate the true nature of the *bacillus icteroides,* which Sanarelli asserted was the specific
cause of yellow fever, and in 1890, when the Army
Commission on yellow fever was appointed, Dr.
Carroll was placed second in command. He sailed
from New York in company with Dr. Reed on
June 21, 1900, and reached Havana on the 25th.
On August 4, when matters were in working train
in Cuba, Dr. Reed returned to the United States

for two months on official business, and Dr. Carroll remained at the head of affairs in Cuba. It was during this interval that he had the attack of yellow fever, described as the first case produced experimentally by the bite of the mosquito. Dr. Carroll himself says that the proudest circumstance of his life is the fact that he was the first person to succumb to mosquito inoculation, although, he adds, " with a wife and five young children at home, my thoughts during the serious part of my illness may be better imagined than described."

During Dr. Carroll's convalescence an incident occurred which caused him a good deal of amusement. One of his nurses, who came from Tennessee, had had considerable experience with yellow fever, having, indeed, lost her husband and several children from it. One day early in his illness, Dr. Carroll mentioned to her that he had contracted the disease through the bite of a mosquito and noticed that she looked surprised. Some time later, when well enough to look over the daily records of his condition, he found this entry: " Says he got his illness through the bite of a mosquito—*delirious!* "

Although Dr. Carroll made a rapid recovery from yellow fever, he did not entirely escape its effects. During the course of the illness he had a sudden heart attack, the nature of which is best described in his own words: " From personal experience I think more stress should be laid on the necessity for confining mustard foot-baths to the earliest stage, as laid down by Sternberg and nearly all writers. In my own case it was used for the first time on the third day, and I shall never forget the effect of it. Within half an hour after the removal of the foot-bath, and while I was oppressed with a weight of heavy grey blankets, I felt a sudden pain and embarrassment at the heart. The pain was very acute and accompanied with a feeling of distention, as if the organ was much distended and was being arrested in diastole. Happily, it lasted but a few moments. This was the only time I felt myself to be in imminent danger." [1] Unfortunately, the effects of this attack were not so transitory as Dr. Carroll believed when he first wrote his account of it. Subsequent events have shown that this was, undoubtedly, an acute dilatation of the heart, which has induced a permanent valvular lesion that limits Dr. Carroll's activity and has caused his rejection by a life insurance company.

Early in October, 1900, Dr. Reed returned to Cuba to collect material for the preliminary re-

[1] " The Treatment of Yellow Fever," Jour. Amer. Med. Assoc., July 19, 1902.

port of the Commission. This occupied about ten days, after which he again went back to the United States, where he presented the first results of the work before the American Public Health Association in Indianapolis, at the end of October. Shortly after the 1st of November Dr. Reed was once more in Cuba, and resumed the personal supervision of the work.

All the reports of the Commission bear Dr. Carroll's name as well as that of Dr. Reed, and in reading them we should always bear in mind that, while the experiments were planned by the master mind of the chief, the accuracy with which they were carried out and the care by which all possible precautions were taken to exclude every source of error, are due to Dr. Carroll quite as much as to Dr. Reed.

In February, 1901, when the work at Camp Lazear was finished, Dr. Reed returned to the United States, but Dr. Carroll remained for some weeks longer in order to investigate into the condition of the urine in yellow fever, as well as to ascertain how long the mosquito is capable of conveying the infection. He sailed for home on March 4, but the following August he returned to Cuba alone, having been sent by the United States Government for the purpose of performing the experiments in the inoculation of blood and serum described in Chapter VII. These experiments have already been dwelt upon at some length, but the present seems to be the most appropriate place to relate an incident which shows how greatly the final success of the yellow fever work was due to Dr. Carroll's force of character.

The serious nature of the experimental cases at Las Animas Hospital and the occurrence of two deaths had alarmed Dr. Guiteras and Dr. Finlay and had occasioned no little excitement in the public mind. Such a condition of things would have deterred many men from further action, but Dr. Carroll was of a different fibre. To be driven from the field of battle just as the crowning success of his investigations was at hand was not a part of his plan; his continuance, however, was rendered somewhat difficult by the fact that Dr. Reed, disturbed by the exaggerated reports which reached him through the press, and hampered in his judgment by the disadvantage of being at a distance, wrote to advise against further experiments upon human beings, and Dr. Carroll was forced to stand alone. The correspondence between them at this juncture makes it plain that the Yellow Fever Commission owes the completion of the final stage in its work at this particular time to Dr. Carroll's wisdom and self-reliance.

On August 18, Dr. Carroll wrote to Dr. Reed

as follows concerning the serious character of the yellow fever cases then under Dr. Guiteras' care:

LAS ANIMAS HOSPITAL, HAVANA,
Aug. 18, 1901.

MY DEAR DOCTOR: The first fatal case of experimental fever is now on record. Dr. Guiteras' second case died at 2 P. M. this morning, on the sixth day of the disease, after having had black vomit, with delirium, bloody stools, etc. . . . Guiteras declined to permit the case to be autopsied, for fear of its effect upon the Spaniards. The morgue is situated adjoining to and continuous with the laboratory, and is completely screened with slatted windows. Dr. Gorgas came out later and overcame the objections, so I made the autopsy in Dr. Guiteras' presence, and with his assistance. . . .

Their third case has black vomit, hiccough, convulsive movements, delirium, and will die within twenty-four hours. The fourth and fifth cases are down, the former very mild, in the person of Dr. G.'s laboratory assistant, and the latter, a Miss Mears, a nurse, came down to-day. So far she seems to be one of only moderate severity. . . . In the third case there was no rise of temperature until within the first three hours of the sixth day of the disease. I was prepared to take blood from this individual on the second day, but Guiteras would not let me bite him with the six insects which I had ready for the purpose. To tell the truth, they appear to be panic-stricken at the positive character of their results, and they think all biting should be stopped.

Very sincerely yours,
JAMES CARROLL.

This letter crossed the following, coming from Dr. Reed to Dr. Carroll:

BLUE RIDGE SUMMIT, PA.,
Aug. 23, 1901.

MY DEAR DOCTOR: Guiteras and my good friend Dr. Finlay must have been having a devil of a time with their patients, as far as I can judge by the accounts in the daily papers. I wonder what they think of the "mild" character of the attacks conveyed by these insects! There did not appear to be much "immunity conveyed by these insects." Really, this sacrifice of life was so unnecessary, in my opinion. I was certain that somebody was bound to be killed before the work was completed.

You say "prospects favourable." And this leads me to strongly advise against further experiments on human beings. Our work has been too good to be marred now by a death. As much as I should like to know whether the filtrate will convey the disease, I should advise against it. Infect as many insects as you can for further sectioning, and get other information about the epidemic at Santiago de las Vegas, and send me as soon as you can.

Please extend my sympathy to Drs. G. and Finlay, with my kindest regards. I return to Washington September 1.

Yours sincerely,
WALTER REED.

It will be remembered that in all the inoculation experiments carried on at Camp Lazear no

fatal case of experimental yellow fever had occurred, and Dr. Carroll was convinced that it was
entirely possible for him to continue the experiments necessary to the completion of his work
without unjustifiable risk to life, the death at Las
Animas being due, in his opinion, to special causes
which it would be within his power to control. To
abandon his researches simply because the public
mind was unduly agitated was not to be thought
of. Accordingly, during the interval between the
despatch of his letter to Dr. Reed and the receipt
of the one which crossed it, he proceeded with
the work along the proposed lines, writing again
on August 22 to keep Dr. Reed informed of his
proceedings. About a week later he received the
following letter from Reed:

> BLUE RIDGE SUMMIT, PA.,
> Aug. 27, 1901.
>
> MY DEAR CARROLL: I have your letters of the 18th
> and the 23d, both of which reached me by this morn-
> ing's mail. It is needless to say that both are of extreme
> interest. Certainly, Guiteras should now be satisfied with
> his proof of the mosquito theory. Six out of seven cases,
> with two fatal, is evidence that should convince even
> Wasdin. I wrote you a few days ago advising against
> further experiments on human beings, in view of these
> fatal cases. From the tenor of your last letter, however,
> I see that you have made all preparations to go ahead
> with the observations as determined by us at Washing-

ton, and I hardly know what to say. I will suggest that, inasmuch as the injection of the blood has given us four positive results, you limit your observations to the injection of the serum without making controls injected with unfiltered blood. If the filtrate proves negative in, say, three or four cases, that would decide the point conclusively.

Of course, since Guiteras denied you the chance to obtain the blood, I suppose you must obtain your first subject by means of the mosquito's bite, unless there are cases at Havana. What could have been Guiteras' objection to your applying mosquitoes to his cases? . . . I shall await your results with the greatest interest.

Please remember me kindly to Majors Havard and Gorgas, and to Agramonte when you see him.

Sincerely yours,
WALTER REED.

This letter was written on August 27, and after writing it Dr. Reed made up his mind, on further reflection, that it would be unwise to interfere with Dr. Carroll's plans, considering that since he was on the spot he was, after all, the best judge as to the propriety of making further experiments upon human beings. On August 29, therefore, he cabled to Dr. Carroll as follows:

WASHINGTON, D. C.,
Aug. 29, 1901.

Consult Havard. Use your best judgment in future.

REED.

This despatch was received by Dr. Carroll on the same day as the letter written on the 27th, and was a great relief to his mind. He had some difficulty at first in producing the necessary experimental cases; in spite of delay from this cause, however, as well as hindrances of various kinds, among them the accident to the suction pump, already described, he persevered according to the proposed plans and completed the work in the latter part of October. Dr. Reed's last letter to him before his return home shows emphatically how satisfactory were the results of his judgment at this final stage of the yellow fever work:

SURGEON GENERAL'S OFFICE,
WASHINGTON, D. C., Oct. 26, 1901.

MY DEAR DOCTOR: I have just received your letter of the 22d, and hasten to congratulate you on the thorough manner in which you have accomplished the task assigned you. The results could not be better, and throw a flood of light on the etiology of yellow fever. . . . We can now go ahead and submit a contribution on the etiology of yellow fever. This we must do promptly, after we have discussed all of the later results. . . .

Again congratulations. Hoping to see you soon,
Very sincerely yours,
W. REED.

The published report of these experiments is the last paper issued under the joint names of Reed and Carroll. With its appearance the official publications of the Commission ended, but Dr. Carroll's interest in the subject has continued unabated, and he has embodied the knowledge acquired during his unique experiences in several papers of the greatest interest. The first of these, on " The Treatment of Yellow Fever," published in July, 1902, is of special interest, because it is the first discussion of the therapeutics of the disease since its ætiology has been correctly known. After reviewing all the methods of treatment employed both in ancient and more modern times, Dr. Carroll lays down the following general principles: [2]

In yellow fever we are dealing with a disease of short duration and one that tests severely the vital powers of the patient. I believe, however, that in previously healthy, non-debilitated subjects, free from organic lesions, the mortality can be reduced, practically to zero, by careful and judicious treatment instituted at the incipiency of the attack. On the other hand, if there be present debility from any cause, anæmia, organic lesions of the heart, liver, or kidneys, the outlook is always serious and recovery doubtful. The treatment must be essentially eliminative and supporting, with the incidental use of measures tending to reduce hyperpyrexia, relieve pain, and remove internal congestions.

[2] Jour. Amer. Med. Assoc., July 19, 1902.

" The lesions and symptoms," he continues, " are produced by a powerful toxin circulating in the blood and tissue fluids. This poison appears to act with greatest intensity upon the liver, and next upon the kidneys." After giving an able description of the conspicuous pathological lesions produced by the disease, Dr. Carroll proceeds as follows:

The primary indication in the treatment of yellow fever is to remove the immediate cause of the condition present, *viz.*, the toxin. This is best and most expeditiously effected through the normal channel, with the urinary secretion, aided by the moderately free action of the skin and moderate depletion of the digestive tract by the use of mild saline cathartics. With the evacuation of these fluids and the toxin they contain, the symptoms abate—speaking of the early stage—and the stomach will retain an increased amount of fluid to replace that which has been removed. Care should be taken to maintain one or more of these functions throughout the attack, sustaining the patient's strength by the judicious use of appropriate stimulants. It is much to be regretted that we have no means of acting directly on the liver.

After reviewing the various means of fulfilling these indications in detail, Dr. Carroll takes up the question of nutrition during the disease:

The nutrition of the patient is a subject well worthy of consideration. Food is frequently withheld for varying periods, from three to five days or a week; in my own case, I think for at least eight days nothing was allowed but water, Apollinaris, ice, and champagne. Now, during all this time certain cells of the body are functioning and using up their own protoplasm, for in conditions of anæmia or malnutrition and in the infectious diseases, we know that the cells of the vital organs undergo degeneration and often necrosis, from want of proper material. In specific fevers the functions of some of the cells are consumed in the performance of these functions and converted into waste material and end-products which add to the general intoxication. Physiologists teach us that there are certain foods that will prevent this by saving their proteid constituents. Among these are gelatine, fat, and non-proteid foods, the latter of which, in the form of olive oil, has been used with marked success by Spanish physicians in the treatment of yellow fever. . . . The rationale of this treatment appears to be that the oil is highly nutritious, a proteid saver, and is readily absorbed by the epithelial and endothelial cells of the capillaries. In this way the integrity of the latter is preserved and the hæmorrhage prevented. Pathology teaches us that when there is capillary blood stasis, hæmorrhage soon takes place from deprivation of nourishment, the endothelial cells of the capillaries being nourished by the blood that circulates within the vessels. This suggests the early administration of olive oil in emulsion with lime water.

Finally, Dr. Carroll takes up the question of decrease in the elimination of urea as follows:

The early involvement of the liver, as indicated by the early lesion in the duodenum, naturally suggests an

cluding, Dr. Carroll makes reference to some experiments, performed a hundred years ago, which have great historic interest in the light of our present knowledge.

They were made by a student of the University of Pennsylvania, Stubbins Ffirth by name, who embodied a description of them in a graduation thesis presented on June 6, 1804. During the epidemics of 1802 and 1803 in Philadelphia, Ffirth made numerous attempts to inoculate himself by depositing fresh black vomit and blood obtained from patients in the early stages of the disease into incisions made in his arms and legs. Besides numerous other experiments he inserted four drops of such serum into an incision in his leg. One must read this interesting treatise in order to appreciate fully the determination of the investigator, who administered black vomit to animals, injected it into his own circulation, and deposited it in his own tissues. He inhaled the fumes of six ounces of this material which he heated over a sand-bath in a small room; the residue he made into pills and swallowed. Failing in this, he further tried to inoculate himself with blood serum, saliva, perspiration, bile, and urine, and finally concluded that yellow fever was neither infectious nor contagious. Since the French Commission has told us that 0.1 cc. of virulent serum is sufficient to infect, we can safely say that Stubbins Ffirth came very near to proving the inoculability of yellow fever more than a century ago.

It is greatly to be hoped that Dr. Carroll will continue the line of investigation in which he has achieved such signal success. The fact that the specific germ of yellow fever is almost certainly ultra-microscopic, makes it very improbable that we shall discover it, at least with the means now at our command. But there are great possibilities for investigation as to the transmission of other diseases through the medium of insects, and the establishment of prophylaxis along lines suggested by such demonstrations. In this connection it is interesting to learn from Dr. Carroll that Dr. Reed firmly believed that smallpox is conveyed by a biting insect of some kind, and that he and Dr. Carroll made some (apparently ineffectual) attempts to variolate calves by causing them to be bitten by bed-bugs that had previously been applied to patients suffering with smallpox.

I cannot close this little memoir of Dr. Carroll more suitably than by quoting from an address delivered by Dr. J. W. Pilcher, U. S. A., before the Association of Military Surgeons touching " The Duty of the Physician to the Public," in which he alludes to Dr. Carroll as follows:

" While stationed in the Far West some years ago, my attention was attracted by the unusual ability of a young soldier who had come under my command. Believing that a higher fate might be in store for him than that of an enlisted man of the army, I began instructing him in the art of medicine. He became very

much interested in the subject, and under my direction
pursued the work until he acquired the degree of Doctor
of Medicine and ultimately became employed as assistant in the Army Medical Museum at Washington.
When the entrance of our army into Cuba made the con-
quest of yellow fever one of the most important forces
to be accomplished, he and his chief, the late, lamented
Walter Reed, determined to enter upon a series of investigations in that direction. The proper execution of
the work demanded animal experimentation of the
highest type. Humanity must be the subject. No crea-
ture of a lower grade would suffice. In the grandeur of
self-sacrifice this glorious fellow submitted himself to
the bite of a *stegomyia fasciata* from the sick room of
a yellow fever patient. The disease promptly developed
in its most severe form. . . . Only the most intimate
care of the ablest physicians based upon a constitution
strengthened by correct living and good habits saved
him from the fell destroyer.

" From this experiment grew that wonderful series
of studies upon which has been based the true theory
of the control of yellow fever. I refer to the particular
case because I am prouder than I can state that the results of my teaching have brought into the profession
a man so highly typical of the best in practice and in
experimentation. That this example was followed by
Jesse Lazear, in whom the experiment resulted fatally
and whose brilliant young life was sacrificed for the
benefit of the people of America, is but an additional
demonstration of the great danger which this young
physician incurred, without hope of reward, for the
benefit of the human race."

I subjoin a list of the articles which Dr. Carroll has published independently on the subject of yellow fever.

LIST OF DR. CARROLL'S INDEPENDENT CONTRIBUTIONS TO THE LITERATURE OF YELLOW FEVER.

"The Treatment of Yellow Fever." Jour. Amer. Med. Assoc., July 19, 1902.

"The Transmission of Yellow Fever." Jour. Amer. Med. Assoc., May 23, 1903.

"The Etiology of Yellow Fever: an Addendum." Jour. Amer. Med. Assoc., Nov. 28, 1903.

"Remarks on the History, Cause, and Mode of Transmission of Yellow Fever, etc." Jour. Assoc. Military Surgeons, 1903.

"A Brief Review of the Etiology of Yellow Fever." N. Y. Med. Jour. and Phil. Med. Jour. (consol.), Feb. 6 and 13, 1904.

"Yellow Fever: a Popular Lecture." Amer. Med., June 3, 1905.

"Lessons to be Learned from the Present Outbreak of Yellow Fever." Jour. Amer. Med. Assoc., Oct. 7, 1905.

"Remarks on the Epidemics of Yellow Fever in Baltimore." Old Maryland, Feb., 1906.

"Without Mosquitoes There Can Be No Yellow Fever." American Medicine, March 17, 1906.

JESSE W. LAZEAR

Dr. Jesse W. Lazear, the third member of the Army Commission, was born in Baltimore on May

2, 1866. His early education was received at Trinity Hall, a private school in Washington, Pennsylvania, from which he entered the Johns Hopkins University, graduating in 1889. He then studied medicine at Columbia University and was graduated there in 1892, after which he served for two years at the Bellevue Hospital, New York. When his hospital service ended he spent a year in Europe, part of which was passed at the Pasteur Institute, in Paris. On his return to this country he was appointed bacteriologist to the medical staff of the Johns Hopkins Hospital, and also held the position of assistant in clinical microscopy in the University.

Much of Dr. Lazear's time after he was graduated in medicine was spent in research, and during his residence at Bellevue he succeeded in isolating, for the first time, the diplococcus of Neisser in pure culture from the circulating blood, in a case of ulcerative endocarditis; he followed up this discovery by investigations into problems connected with malarial parasites. He was the first person in this country to confirm and elaborate the studies of Romanovsky and others concerning the intimate structures of the hæmatozoa of malaria, although his work on the subject was, unfortunately, not published until after his death. He, together with Woolley and Thayer, was first in this country to

JESSE W. LAZEAR, M.D.

Member of the U. S. A. Yellow Fever Commission, who laid
down his life on the field of service

confirm, in part, the work of Ross and the Italians on the mosquito cycle of the malarial parasite.

The years spent in studies of this description had, of course, peculiarly fitted Dr. Lazear for the work which the Yellow Fever Commission was instituted to conduct, and he was appointed to it with the rank of acting assistant surgeon. When Dr. Reed, in company with Dr. Carroll, reached Cuba, Dr. Lazear had been on the island several months, during which time he had observed a number of cases of yellow fever, performing autopsies, when opportunity afforded, and taking cultures. He had studied many films of blood from yellow fever patients, and was prepared to say with confidence that cultures and blood examinations promised nothing of special importance.

Not long after the arrival of the other members of the Commission Dr. Lazear applied to himself a mosquito of the genus *stegomyia,* which had bit- . ten a yellow fever patient some days previously. The results, however, in this instance were negative. About a month later, during Dr. Reed's absence in the United States, Dr. Lazear allowed a mosquito, which had chanced to alight on his hand, to take its fill. This occurrence took place in the yellow fever ward of Las Animas Hospital, in the suburbs of Havana, on September 13. He did not at the time believe that the insect which had bitten

him was a *Culex Fasciatus,* but, as he expressed it,
" a common, ordinary brown mosquito "; nevertheless, as it was not at that time known whether
one genus, or more than one, was capable of conveying the disease, he may be said to have voluntarily accepted all the chances that went with the
inoculation.

Five days later, during the night of September
18, he was seized with a chill, followed in a few
hours by another. Dr. Carroll, who was at that
time recovering from his own attack of yellow
fever, examined Dr. Lazear's blood twice for malarial parasites, and as the results were negative
and the clinical symptoms made the diagnosis
fairly secure, he was removed to the yellow fever
isolation camp. Before his removal he made over
to Dr. Carroll his notes covering all the attempts
at mosquito inoculation, and told him of his personal experience concerning which there was no
record. For three days of his illness he held his
own, but at the end of this time the dreaded black
vomit made its appearance, a symptom the significance of which he himself knew only too well.
" I shall never forget," says Dr. Carroll in his
published account of Dr. Lazear's illness, " the
expression of alarm in his eyes when I last saw
him alive in the third or fourth day of his illness.
The spasmodic contractions of his diaphragm in-

dicated that black vomit was impending, and he fully appreciated their significance." Four days later he died, leaving a widow and two little children, the younger of whom he had never seen.

" Thus ended," says Dr. Carroll, " a life of brilliant promise at the early age of thirty-four. Dr. Lazear died that his fellow-men might live in comfort and happiness. . . . It is no exaggeration to say that hundreds, nay, perhaps thousands, in the Southern States owe their lives, certainly their prosperity, to the results of the work in which he was engaged, and for which he and his family have paid such a fearful penalty. The world lost in him a benefactor; the profession a man of high attainments, noble character, and lovable disposition; words cannot measure the loss to his widow and orphans." These words are taken from Dr. Carroll's address at the unveiling of the memorial tablet to Dr. Lazear at the Johns Hopkins Hospital, and I ought not to close this tribute to his memory without quoting from the remarks of his friend and co-worker, Dr. W. B. Thayer.

" I wish," Dr. Thayer said, " especially for the younger men here, that I might be able to picture to you Lazear as a man and companion. Quiet, retiring, and modest almost to a fault, he was yet a manly man with a good, vigorous temper, well controlled, and a rare physical courage, with a deep love of his profession, and an ardent desire to make adequate contributions to its advance. . . . When the news of his sad death became known, there were those who blamed what they regarded as unjustified temerity; who felt that such risks were not for married men. With these I cannot agree. No man loved his family more than Lazear, but he was engaged in a great work—and he knew it—in a work where at the moment no substitute could take his place. Lazear saw his duty clearly, and where he saw his duty fear and doubt could not enter in. A few well-known lines of Emerson's tell the story:

> *Though love repine and reason chafe,*
> *There comes a voice without reply.*
> *'Tis man's perdition to be safe,*
> *When for the truth he ought to die.*"

Dr. Lazear laid down his life before the Yellow Fever Commission had well entered upon their work, so early in its career, indeed, that his name appears in only one of its published reports, the " Preliminary Note on the Etiology of Yellow Fever." Nevertheless, although his untimely death deprived him of a full share in the brilliant results they achieved, he did heroic service in the cause. I do not think I can close this brief memorial more appropriately than by citing the tribute paid him by his friend and colleague, Dr. Reed, when addressing the Medical and Chirurgical Faculty of Maryland in April, 1901.

Before proceeding to the discussion of my subject, it is fitting that I should pay brief tribute to the memory of a former member of this Faculty, the late Dr. Jesse W. Lazear, United States Army. I can hardly trust myself to speak of my late colleague, since the mention of his name brings back such scenes of anxiety and depression as one recalls only with pain. Along with these sad memories, however, come other recollections of a manly and fearless devotion to duty such as I have never seen equalled. In the discharge of the latter, Dr. Lazear seemed absolutely tireless and quite oblivious of self. Filled with an earnest enthusiasm for the advancement of his profession and for the cause of science, he let no opportunity pass unimproved. Although the evening might find him discouraged over the difficulties at hand, with the morning's return he again took up the task full of eagerness and hope. During a service of less than a year in Cuba he won the goodwill and respect of his brother officers and the affection of his immediate associates. Almost at the beginning of what promised to be a life full of usefulness and good works he was suddenly stricken, and, dying, added one more name to that imperishable roll of honour in which none others belong than martyrs to the cause of humanity. It is my own earnest wish that, whatever credit may hereafter be given to the work of the American Commission in Cuba, during the past year, the name of my late colleague, Dr. Lazear, may be always associated therewith.

Dr. Lazear's remains lie in the Loudon Park Cemetery at Baltimore. A memorial tablet, erected by his friends at the Johns Hopkins Hospital, bears this inscription, by President Eliot:

In memory of
JESSE WILLIAM LAZEAR,
born May 2, 1866, at Baltimore,
Graduated in Arts at
the Johns Hopkins University in 1889;
and in Medicine at Columbia University in 1892.
In 1895-96 Assistant Resident Physician
in the Johns Hopkins Hospital.
Member of the Yellow Fever Commission in 1900
with the rank of Acting Assistant Surgeon.
He died of Yellow Fever at Quemados, Cuba,
28 of September, 1900.
With more than the courage and devotion of
the soldier, he risked and lost his life to show
how a fearful pestilence is communicated and
how its ravages may be prevented.

ARISTIDES AGRAMONTE

Dr. Aristides Agramonte was born in Puerto Principe, Cuba, on June 3, 1868. His father was the well-known insurgent, General Eduardo Agramonte, who was killed in battle on March 8, 1872. After General Agramonte's death his family emigrated to the United States, where the son received

ARISTIDES AGRAMONTE, M.D.

Member of the U. S. A. Yellow Fever Commission. From a photograph taken in 1902

his education, first in the public schools and then in the College of the City of New York. He studied medicine in the College of Physicians and Surgeons and graduated there with honour on June 8, 1890, receiving the third Harston prize for clinical reports.

After obtaining his degree Dr. Agramonte held several appointments in the city of New York, two of which he obtained through competitive examination. One of these was as sanitary inspector in the new health department, the other as assistant bacteriologist to the health department.

In May, 1898, he was appointed acting assistant surgeon in the United States Army, and in that capacity he was sent to Santiago in July of the same year. In the following November he returned, and after presenting a report of the investigations made by him at Santiago, he was sent to Havana, in December, to make studies in the bacteriology of yellow fever; the results of which were published in the Medical News for February, 1900.

In May, 1901, he was put in charge of the army laboratory of the Division of Cuba, a post which he retained till the end of his service on the island. At the same time he was also appointed a member of the Army Commission on yellow fever, with Dr. Reed, Dr. Carroll, and Dr. Lazear.

During the summer of 1900 Dr. Agramonte investigated an epidemic of yellow fever at Santa Clara, Cuba, as well as certain cases of so-called pernicious fever at Pinar del Rio. The latter proved to be an epidemic of yellow fever in a garrison of 800 troops, and as the cases were being treated for malaria by the medical officers in charge, Dr. Agramonte met with a great deal of opposition when he announced a contrary opinion. For his determined stand in carrying out his views in the face of obstacles and for the general excellence of his work he was publicly complimented by his commanding officer.

Dr. Agramonte's part in the work of the Yellow Fever Commission, as I have already said, was that of the pathological work and the autopsies; and he was associated with the commission until the return of Reed and Carroll to the United States in February, 1901.

In August, 1900, Dr. Agramonte received the degree of M. D. from the Medical Faculty of Havana, after passing incorporation examinations, and in the September following he obtained, by competitive examination, the chair of bacteriology and experimental pathology in the same institution, a post which he still holds.

The "Preliminary" and the "Additional Notes" in which the Army Commission published the results of their labours, as well as their paper on " Experimental Yellow Fever," bear Dr. Agramonte's name, with those of the other members of the board. Dr. Agramonte has, moreover, published several valuable articles on the subject independently, a list of which I give below. He has also issued a number of papers on subjects other than yellow fever, which I have not space to record.

LIST OF DR. AGRAMONTE'S INDEPENDENT CONTRIBUTIONS TO THE LITERATURE OF YELLOW FEVER.

" El Bac. Icteroides (Sanarelli) y el Bac. X (Sternberg)." Ext. of an Official Report. Crónica Médico-Chirurgica, Havana, Oct., 1899.

" La Relacion del Bacilo Icteroides con la Fiebre Amarilla." El Progréso Méd., Havana, March, 1900.

" El Fracaso del Suero Sanarelli." Revista de Med. y Chir., Havana, March, 1900.

" Report of Bacteriological Investigations upon Yellow Fever." The Med. News, February, 1900.

" Paludismo y Fiebre Amarilla: Seis Casos Clínicos." El Progréso Méd., Havana, Oct., 1900.

" Anotaciones acera de la Etiologia de la Fiebre Amarilla." Revista de Med. y Chir., Aug., 1901.

" La Etiolgía de la Fiebre Amarilla." Official Report to the N. Y. Quarantine Department, Revista de Med. Tropical, October 1, 1902.

" The Supposed Parasite of Yellow Fever." Revista Méd., Cubana, October, 1902.

CONCLUSION

I would the great world grew like thee
Who grewest not alone in power
And knowledge, but by year and hour
In reverence and in charity.

    .   .   .   .   .

The flame is quenched that I foresaw,
The head hath missed an earthly wreath;
I curse not nature, no, nor death,
For nothing is that errs from law.

We pass; the path that each man trod
Is dim, or will be dim with weeds;
What fame is left for human deeds
In endless ages rests with God.
            —TENNYSON. *In Memoriam.*

THIS little volume is my tribute to the memory of a great and good man. My own acquaintance with Dr. Reed was, I regret to say, but a brief one, yet it made upon me that lasting impression which was a characteristic of his personality, and which I count among the good things of my life. The following letter I prize, not only because it is the only one I ever received from him, but because it contains a reference to his life-work.

WAR DEPARTMENT,
SURGEON GENERAL'S OFFICE,
ARMY MEDICAL MUSEUM AND LIBRARY,
WASHINGTON.

July 15, 1901

My dear Dr. Kelly;
Absence from the City will account for my delay in acknowledging receipt of your kind letter of the 10th inst. Please accept my sincere thanks for your thoughtfulness in sending me this old paper on yellow fever, which had not been brought to my notice —

Sincerely, yours,
Walter Reed

I have tried to set forth in these pages all the benefits which Dr. Reed's talents and industry have accomplished for the world, but I must not lay down my pen without tracing some of the unconscious lessons which such a life holds for his fellowmen.

The annals of Walter Reed's early years are refreshing in their simplicity. They record a natural, healthful life, with habits and interests in no wise different from those of thousands of American boys. Nothing in its circumstances or pursuits marked him out as different from his fellows, and his character was distinguished from theirs, not by flashes and premonitions of genius, but by a remarkable uprightness, earnestness of purpose, and tenderness of heart. Neither his youth nor his mature years were characterised by any of those eccentricities which it is often the fashion to consider inseparably associated with genius; indeed, his whole life is a consistent witness to the falsity of the theory which exempts a man of unusual abilities from the laws governing mankind in general, on the ground that exceptional talent is in itself abnormal. The popular idea that the gifted few are not responsible for their actions, because they are themselves a deviation from the normal, and that what are vices in their fellow-men are venial errors in them, finds no support in Walter Reed's

was that he might be permitted to alleviate in some
degree the suffering of humanity, and all his efforts
were spent in striving toward this goal, without a
thought of self.

Walter Reed's work here is over; his humble,
faithful use of the talents committed to his charge
is at an end, and he has entered into his reward.
When we are tempted to mourn over his untimely
death, and to regret all the possibilities which a
farther use of his abilities might have developed,
we should remember the words of Bishop Lawrence of Massachusetts to Mrs. Reed, after her
husband's death: " Let us try to feel that the Master took him because he had other work for him to
do." Are not the talents, which to our feeble intelligence seem so greatly needed by our present
necessities, still employed in the Master's service
in ways beyond our finite understanding?

> " O strong soul, by what shore
>   Tarriest thou now? For that force,
> Surely, has not been left vain!
> Somewhere, surely, afar,
> In the sounding labour-house vast
> Of being, is practised that strength,
> Zealous, beneficent, firm! "

BIBLIOGRAPHY *

REED, WALTER. [1851-1902.]

1892.—The contagiousness of erysipelas. *Boston M. and S. J.*, v. 126 (10), March 10, p. 237.

1893.—Remarks on the cholera spirillum. [An address before Ramsey County Medical Society, March 28.] *Northwest. Lancet*, St. Paul, (297), v. 13 (9), May 1, pp. 161-164.

1894a.—Association of *Proteus vulgaris* with *Diplococcus lanceolatus* in a case of croupous pneumonia. *Johns Hopkins Hosp. Bull.*, Baltimore, v. 5 (34), March, pp. 24-25.

1894b.—The germicidal value of trikresol. *St. Louis M. and S. J.* (642), v. 66 (6), June, pp. 329-337.

1894c.—Idem. *Proc. Ass. Mil. Surg. U. S.* (Washington), St. Louis, v. 4, pp. 199-208.

1894d.—A brief contribution to the identification of *Streptococcus erysipelatos. Boston M. and S. J.*, v. 131 (14), October 4, pp. 339-340.

1895a.—An investigation into the so-called lymphoid nodules of the liver in typhoid fever. *Johns Hopkins Hosp. Rep.*, Baltimore, v. 5, pp. 379-396.

1895b.—An investigation into the so-called lymphoid nodules of the liver in abdominal typhus. *Am. J. M. Sc.*, Philadelphia, n. s., v. 110, pp. 543-559.

1895c.—What credence should be given to the statements of those who claim to furnish vaccine lymph free of bacteria? [Read before the District of Columbia Md. Soc., June 5.] *J. Pract. M.*, N. Y., v. 5 (12), July, pp. 532-534.

1896a.—[The character, prevalence, and probable causation of the malarial fevers at Washington Barracks and Fort Myer.] Rep. Surg. Gen. Army, Wash., pp. 65-77, 1 diagram, 1 table.

1896b.—The parasite of malaria. *J. Pract. M.*, N. Y., v. 6 (9), Apr., pp. 382-383.

* This bibliography is adopted from that issued by tne Medical Society of the District of Columbia in their published account of the Memorial Services to Dr. Reed, December 31, 1902.

1897a.—Serum diagnosis in typhoid fever. Rep. Surg. Gen. Army, Wash., pp. 68-73.

1897b.—On the appearance of certain amœboid bodies in the blood of vaccinated monkeys (*Rhoesus*) and children, and in the blood of variola. An experimental study. *Tr. Ass. Am. Physicians,* Phila., v. 12, pp. 291-302, 2 pls.

1897c.—On the appearance of certain amœboid bodies in the blood of vaccinated monkeys (*Rhoesus*) and children, and in the blood from cases of variola. An experimental study. *J. Exper. M.,* N. Y., v. 2 (5), Sept., pp. 515-527, pls. 38-40.

1897d.—Typhoid fever in the District of Columbia; diagnosis: The value of Widal's test, the dried blood method. *Nat. M. Rev.,* Wash., v 7 (6), Nov., pp. 144-146.

1897e.—[Experiments with Hollister's formaldehyde generator.] Rep. Surg. Gen. Army, Wash., pp. 103-104.

1898.—Splenic leukaemia. [*Trans. Med. Soc. District of Columbia,* Oct. 27, 1897.] *Nat. M. Rev.,* Wash. v. 7 (9), Feb., pp. 265-266.

1900.—Report on the practical use of electrozone as a disinfectant in the city of Havana, Cuba. Rep. Surg. Gen. Army, Wash., pp. 178-186. [MS., dated Apr. 20.]

1901a.—The propagation of yellow fever; observations based on recent researches. [Address before 103d Ann. Meeting Med. and Chir. Fac., State of Md., Balt., Apr. 24-27.] *Med. Rec.,* N. Y. (1605), v. 60 (6), Aug. 10, pp. 201-209, tables 1, 2.

1901b.—Idem. Rep. Surg. Gen. Army, Wash., pp. 187-202, 1 pl., 6 fever charts.

1902.—Recent researches concerning the etiology, propagation and prevention of yellow fever, by the United States Army Commission. *J. Hyg.,* Cambridge, Eng., v. 2. (2), Apr. 1, pp. 101-119, charts 1-3.

REED, WALTER, and CARROLL, JAMES.

1899a.—*Bacillus icteroides and Bacillus cholerae suis.* A preliminary note. *Med. News,* N. Y., v. 74 (17), Apr. 29, pp. 513-514.

1899b.—The specific cause of yellow fever. A reply to Dr. G. Sanarelli. *Med. News,* N. Y., v. 75 (11), Sept. 9, pp. 321-329.

1900.—A comparative study of the biological characters and pathogenesis of *Bacillus x* (Sternberg), *Bacillus icteroides* (Sanarelli), and the hog-cholera bacillus (Salmon and Smith). [Received for publication Feb. 25.] *J. Exper. M.* [Balt.], v. 5 (3), Dec. 15, pp. 215-270, figs. a-o, pl. 19, figs. 1-3.

1901.—The prevention of yellow fever. [Read at 29th Ann. Meeting, Am. Pub. Health Ass., Buffalo, Sept. 16-21.] *Med. Rec.,* N. Y. (1616), v. 60 (17), Oct. 26, pp. 641-649, figs. 1-10.

1902.—The etiology of yellow fever. A supplemental note. [Read at 3d Ann. Meeting, Soc. Am. Bacteriologists, Chicago, Dec. 31, 1901, and Jan. 1, 1902.] *Am. Med.,* Phila., v. 3 (8), Feb. 22, pp. 301-305, charts 1-6.

REED, WALTER; CARROLL, JAMES, and AGRAMONTE, ARISTIDES.

1901a.—The etiology of yellow fever. An additional note. [Read at Pan-Am. Med. Cong., Havana, Cuba, Feb. 4-7.] *J. Am. Med. Ass.,* Chicago, v. 36 (7), Feb. 16, pp. 431-440, charts 1-6.

1901b.—Experimental yellow fever. *Am. Med.,* Phila., v. 2 (1), July 6, pp. 15-23, charts 1-8, tables 1-2.

REED, WALTER; CARROLL, JAMES; AGRAMONTE, ARISTIDES, and LAZEAR, JESSE W.

1900.—The etiology of yellow fever. A preliminary note. [Read at Meeting of Am. Pub. Health Ass., Indianapolis, Ind., Oct. 22-26.] *Phila. M. J.* (148), v. 6 (17), Oct. 27, pp. 790-796, tables 1-3, charts 1-2.

REED, WALTER, and STERNBERG, GEORGE M.

1895.—Report of immunity against vaccination conferred upon the monkey by the use of the serum of the vaccinated calf and monkey. *Tr. Ass. Am. Physicians,* Phila., v. 10, pp. 57-69.

INDEX

INDEX